OFFSET PRESS TROUBLES

(Sheet-Fed Presses)

By

ROBERT F. REED

Issued by

GRAPHIC ARTS TECHNICAL FOUNDATION, INC.

4615 Forbes Avenue   Pittsburgh, Pa. 15213

501 $5.00

Copyright 1962 by

LITHOGRAPHIC TECHNICAL FOUNDATION, INC.

Library of Congress Catalog Card Number: 62—21198

Revised Edition, November, 1963
Reprinted, 1967

Issued by

GRAPHIC ARTS TECHNICAL FOUNDATION, INC.
4615 Forbes Avenue   Pittsburgh, Pa. 15213

FOREWORD

Modern offset lithography is a process of many steps starting with copy to be reproduced and ending with printed sheets or articles manufactured from them. In many shops, it is an integrated process, that is, all steps in the process are carried out by men in one organization working co-operatively. In other shops, only part of the process is performed. For example, some shops do only the actual printing, and the other steps are carried out by separate companies or "trade shops." These specialize in photography or plate-making or both, or in finishing operations.

At any rate, production and profits in lithography depend primarily on the output of quality printing by offset presses. Performance of presses is therefore vital to the well being of everyone in the lithographic business.

Offset presses are complicated, precision-built machines. They require knowledge, experience and skill to operate. And how well they perform depends primarily on preventive maintenance, proper make-ready and operation, and the ability of the pressman and his crew to foresee and avoid troubles or to quickly trace them to their sources and remove the causes.

Preventive maintenance and proper operation are covered respectively in LTF Publications #513, "Advanced Pressmanship" and #505/6 "Lithographic Offset Press Operating." The present text discusses the many troubles encountered in sheet-fed offset presswork, their causes, prevention and remedies. It is essentially a revision and expansion of the publication, "Offset Press Troubles" by D. J. MacDonald, issued in 1944. Since that date there have been many changes and improvements. Some of the old troubles have all but disappeared while new ones have arisen. These changes make necessary many changes in and additions to LTF's original text.

In the meantime, web-offset presses have been widely adopted by the industry. While some of the troubles encountered with them are the same as for sheet-fed presses, many are quite different. To avoid confusion, these will be discussed in another LTF publication.

The author is greatly indebted to the following persons for their helpful criticism and suggestions in preparing this manuscript:

Mr. Michael H. Bruno, LTF

Mr. John J. Dougherty, Western Printing & Lithographing Co.

Mr. Anthony C. Genovese, LTF

Dr. Paul J. Hartsuch, LTF

Mr. Charles W. Latham, Consultant

Mr. William A. Pakan, Carnegie Institute of Technology

Mr. George B. Rodenheiser, The David Rankin Jr. School of Mechanical Trades, Saint Louis

Mr. Charles Shapiro, Hopper Paper Co.

Mr. William J. Stevens, National Association of Photo-Lithographers

Mr. C. O. Tower, Central High School, Cincinnati

TABLE OF CONTENTS

INTRODUCTION

Many different makes and sizes of sheet-fed offset presses are in use today. There are at least seven offset press manufacturers in the United States and a number in Europe. Press sizes vary from 14″ x 20″ to 54″ x 77″. Larger presses have been built, but these are for special purposes and are not regular commercial models. Presses smaller than 14″ x 20″ (offset duplicators) are primarily office equipment. However, many shops use them in limited commercial applications.

The majority of single-color presses are in the smaller sizes, from 14″ x 20″ to 35″ x 45″. Four-color presses are mainly in the larger sizes, from 25″ x 38″ to 54″ x 77″. There are, however, two and three-color presses as small as 20″ x 26″. These have their units at different levels to provide the necessary accessibility. Presses printing more than two colors are usually constructed by adding printing units in line but this is not practical in small sizes since it does not provide sufficient space for access between units.

Courtesy of Harris-Seybold Co.

Figure 1.   Four-color Offset Press

1

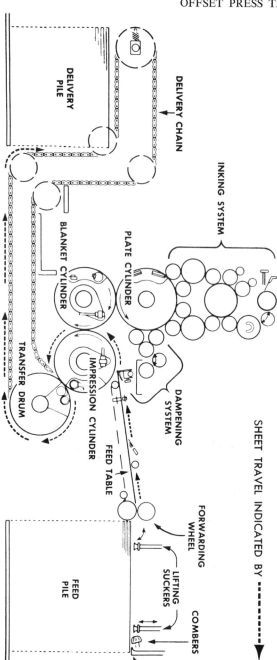

Figure 2.   Diagram of Single-color Offset Press

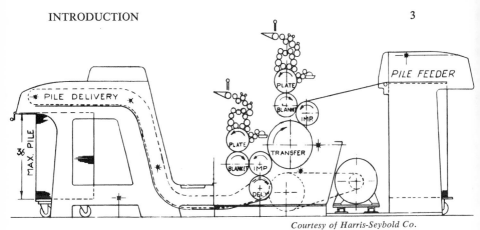

Courtesy of Harris-Seybold Co.

Figure 3.   Diagram of Small Two-color Offset Press

Sheet-fed perfecting presses were formerly built only to order. But because of their increasing popularity, three press manufacturers now supply them in sizes from 18″ x 24″ to 54″ x 78″. In the two British makes, there are no impression cylinders, and the impression is blanket-to-blanket. In the American press, there is an arrangement of cylinders that permits using it to print either two colors one side or one color perfecting. No doubt more sheet-fed perfecting presses will be offered in the near future.

In all American-built presses the plate and blanket cylinders run on bearers. This provides positive meshing of the gears at pitch diameter. When properly set, there is sufficient bearer pressure to overcome any tendency of the bearers to separate due to the necessary packing of the plate and blanket. In European presses, there are either no bearers, or bearers are provided only to enable precise spacing of the plate and blanket cylinders. However, some presses made in Europe for import to the United States have bearers like American-made presses. Each press manufacturer provides instructions regarding the proper cylinder settings and packing of plates and blankets.

Inking systems are fairly standard, with minor variations. For each printing unit there are usually four form rollers, three or four metal vibrating (oscillating) rollers or drums, four or more rubber composition intermediate rollers, one or more steel riders, a ductor roller, fountain roller, and ink fountain. The fountain and ductor rollers meter the ink into the inking system. The rollers and drums are of various diameters so as to distribute the ink evenly in their running direction and prevent streaks. The vibrating drums provide crosswise (lateral) distribution, prevent ridging of the ink,

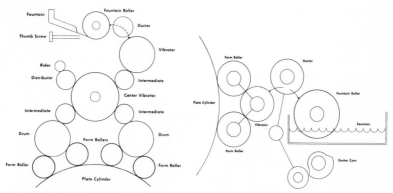

Figure 4.   Diagram of Offset Press
Inking System

Figure 5.   Diagram of
Conventional Dampening System

and reduce the ink's tendency to fly or mist. In recent years, the trend has been toward covering these metal drums with Ebonite, or copper plating them, to reduce their tendency to lose ink receptivity and strip.

Until recently, dampening systems have been quite standard, consisting of two molleton-covered dampening rolls, a metal vibrator or distributing roll, a ductor, fountain roller, and water fountain. Now there are various modifications including parchment paper dampener covers and plastic composition dampeners without covers. There are also new systems including the Mullen and Dahlgren. In the Mullen system, the plate is dampened with an excess of water and the excess squeegeed off by an air knife. In the

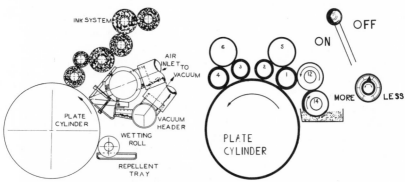

Figure 6.   Diagram Showing Principle of Mullen or Effusor Dampening System

Figure 7.   Diagram of Dahlgren
Dampening System

Dahlgren system, the dampening moisture is applied to the No. 1 ink form roller and not directly to the plate. Variable speed drive of the water-fountain roller is common on newer presses, and a new "brush ductor" that runs continuously in contact with the fountain roller has been introduced.

Single-sheet-by-sheet feeders have been replaced by stream feeders on most modern presses. These cause the sheets to overlap as they proceed down the ramp or feedboard, so that they move at only a fraction of the press speed and are more easily controlled. This enables faster feeding and press speeds of over 7000 sheets per hour are commmon today.

Most sheet feeders feed sheets from the pile and this requires that the press be stopped periodically to receive a new load and have the delivery pile removed. When very long runs are common, presses may be equipped with continuous stream feeders. These, together with dual or continuous delivery, enable the press to be run without stops for loading the feeder or changing the delivery platform.

Accurate register of the sheets with the plate image is all important. It is not only necessary to properly position the work on the sheets, but also to make succeeding impressions fit a first impression. To accomplish this, there is a system of front guides

Courtesy of Harris-Seybold Co.

Figure 8. Feed Rollers

Courtesy of Miehle Printing Press & Mfg. Co.
Figure 9.   Swing Feed

(stops) and side guides to position the sheets. On small presses, tumbler grippers on the impression cylinder catch its front edge and pull it through the impression. On the larger presses, insertion devices are generally feed-roll and swing feed, that push or pick up the sheets and insert them into the impression cylinder grippers. Obviously, timing of the actions of the guides, insertion devices and grippers must be highly accurate.

Figure 10.   Hold-down Brushes on Impression Cylinder

On single-color presses, hold-down brushes are provided. These bear on the impression cylinder just ahead of the impression nip. Their purpose is to hold the sheets snugly against the cylinder and prevent rippling or flapping that would cause premature contact with the offset blanket and a double or slurred impression. On multicolor presses, the hold-down brush is used only on the first printing unit. If used on succeeding units, it would cause smearing. So, on the later units, air blasts are provided to hold sheets snugly against the impression cylinders.

On multicolor presses, provision must be made to transfer the sheets from one printing unit to another in exact register. This is usually done by means of transfer cylinders whose grippers are timed to take hold of the sheets before they are released by the previous cylinder grippers. Thus the sheets are never released until they reach the delivery. Here, not only timing is important, but uniform and proper gripper tension is necessary to prevent sheets from slipping in or pulling out of the grippers anywhere in the system. Any slippage would cause misregister and doubling. And if a sheet were pulled out of the grippers, it would stick to the blanket and possibly be carried up into the inking system.

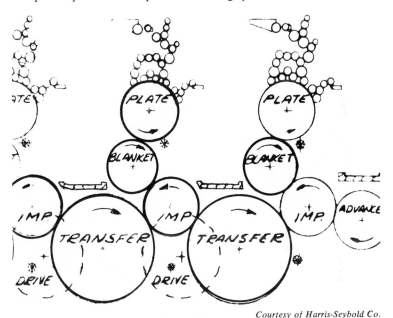

Courtesy of Harris-Seybold Co.

Figure 11.   Diagram Showing Transfer Cylinders on
Harris Multicolor Press

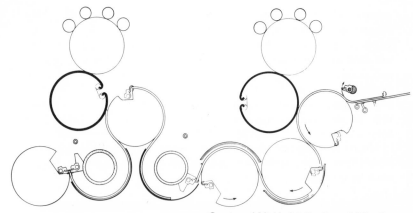

Courtesy of Miehle Printing Press & Mfg. Co.

Figure 12.   Diagram Showing Transfer Cylinders on
Miehle Multicolor Press

The delivery system carries the printed sheets from the last
impression cylinder to the delivery pile where they are jogged. It
starts with a skeleton cylinder which has sprockets at each end that
drive two endless chains carrying gripper bars. These bars are
placed at the proper intervals and timed to receive sheets from the

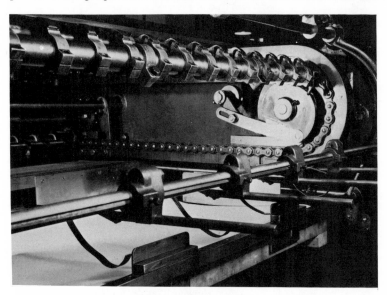

Figure 13.   Chain Delivery

impression cylinder. Their grippers must take a firm hold on the sheets before they are released by the last impression cylinder grippers. Full-size sheets are usually still going through the impression when transfer to the gripper bars occurs. If firm control is lost for even an instant, the sheets will be pulled loose and wrap around the blanket cylinder.

The gripper bars carry the sheets to the delivery pile and drop them in position for jogging. Release is accomplished by means of trip cams which can be easily adjusted to time the drop. Some deliveries have fingers that pick the sheets from the gripper bars, slow them down, and place them against the front gate. Others have vacuum rollers for this purpose.

Courtesy of Miehle Printing Press & Mfg. Co.

Figure 14.   Sheet Delivery Showing Slow-down Fingers

Dual delivery systems consist of two sheet-receiving stations in tandem. The delivery chains extend over both stations and trip cams may be set to release the sheets at either station. Thus the delivery can be continued while skids of printed sheets are being removed from the press. (See Figure 1, page 1.)

The foregoing is a brief, generalized description of the sheet-fed offset press and its essential mechanisms. For a complete and detailed discussion, see LTF Publications No. 505/6 "Lithographic

Offset Press Operating," and No. 513, "Advanced Pressmanship."
Other reading for the offset pressman should include the following
LTF publications:

No. 308   "What the Lithographer Should Know About Paper"
No. 310   "What the Lithographer Should Know About Ink"
No. 318   "The Measurement of Offset Blanket Thickness"
No. 321   "Instruments for Quality Control in Lithography"
No. 803   "pH, What it is, How to Measure it, Where to Use it?"

LTF's plate-making publications, Nos. 804, 805 and 806 also
contain helpful information on overcoming press troubles.

Section 1

Sheet Feed and Delivery Troubles

Successful feeding consists of smooth and consistant operation of the feeder. It depends on how well the paper is piled and lined up in the feeder, and on the proper adjustment of the various feeder elements. These may include combers, separating suckers, forwarding suckers, hold downs, air blasts, forwarding wheels and tapes.

Next, the sheets must be properly registered with the printing unit, and this requires correct adjustment and action of the front guides, side guide, insertion device and impression cylinder grippers. In the case of multicolor presses, two or more impression cylinders are involved together with the necessary transfer cylinders, and all their grippers must be in proper adjustment.

Finally, delivery bar grippers must carry the sheets to the delivery pile and drop them in the correct position to be jogged. Satisfactory press operation therefore depends on the proper adjustment and timing of all sheet handling elements of the press. In addition, the paper must be reasonably flat and free from any pronounced tendency to curl. And, if any one of the necessary conditions is not met, the result is a press trouble that needs to be located and remedied. In some cases this is easy, but in others considerable skill and experience may be required.

The following is a list of the more common feeder and delivery troubles encountered in sheet-fed press operation together with their principal causes and known remedies.

1. The Feeder Fails to Feed Single Sheets

Cause A: The pile is not at the proper feeding height. If too high, it is likely to feed more than one sheet at a time. If too low, it is likely to miss sheets.

REMEDY: Raise or lower the feeder pile until the top sheet is about one-half inch below the top of the forwarding roller, then set the height governor and adjust the combers and suckers.

11

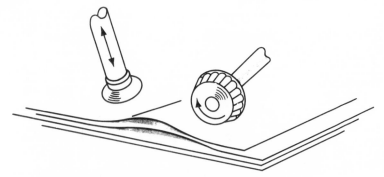

Figure 15.   Diagram Showing Comber and Sheet-separating Sucker

Cause B: Too much separation air blast with nozzle set too low.

REMEDY: Readjust air blast nozzle to proper height and reduce the air pressure.

Cause C: The combers are not set properly.

REMEDY: Be sure the pile height is correct, then reset the combers with just enough pressure to comb the top sheet to a suitable bulge with plenty of clearance between it and the second sheet. If the sheet corners tend to curl up, bend them down during piling. Use wedges, if necessary, to maintain the proper corner height for the combers.

Cause D: The suckers are not performing properly.

REMEDY: With the pile at the proper height and the combers functioning properly, set the separating suckers to just contact the combed bulge of the top sheet inside its crest. This contact should be made with the face of the sucker parallel to the surface of the combed top sheet.

In the case of single-sheet feeders, the front suckers should be set to contact the top sheet as it floats on the separating air. If they push it down on the pile, there is the possibility of picking up two sheets or of missing the sheet completely.

In the case of stream feeders where the forwarding suckers are at the back, they should be so adjusted that the separating suckers lift the sheets to them.

More than one type of sucker is available. Follow the press manufacturer's instructions as to where and when to use each type. Keep the suckers and their actuating mechanisms clean. Use enough vacuum to pick up the sheets but not enough to deform the paper or crack its surface.

Courtesy of Miehle Printing Press & Mfg. Co.

Figure 16.   Sheet Forwarding Suckers

2. The Feeder Forwards Sheets Unevenly

Cause: Too much or too little air blast under the separated top sheet. Too much air ripples the sheet excessively and produces waves between the forwarding wheels that can cause uneven forwarding.

REMEDY: Use just enough air blast to float the top sheet. If the sheets have a tendency to stick, it is better to repile the load, rolling the lifts to free the sheets, rather than try to separate them with excess air.

Courtesy of Miehle Printing Press & Mfg. Co.

Figure 17.   Sheet Forwarding Wheels

3. Oil From Air Compressor Stains Sheets on the Feeder

Cause: An overheated or improperly oiled compressor. It can over-heat due to neglect, use of the wrong type of oil, or running at too high a pressure. When overheated, the oil vaporizes and then con-denses back into oil while going through the blower pipes.

REMEDY: Follow the press instruction manual on oiling and maintaining pumps. Adjust the relief valve so as to keep the air pressure at the proper level.

4. Sheets Cock or Jam on the Conveyor

Cause A: On a single-sheet feeder, the two forwarding wheels do not drop at exactly the same time.

REMEDY: Adjust timing of the wheels.

Cause B: On a single-sheet-by-sheet feeder, tension on the two forwarding wheels is not equal.

REMEDY: Readjust the tension. The farther apart the for-warding wheels, the more critical the adjustment.

Cause C: The rubber rims of the forwarding wheels are not true or are dented.

REMEDY: Put new rubbers on the wheels. Also, set wheels on the forwarding roller and not on or close to the tapes.

Cause D: Tapes become frayed or develop small breaks, or their stitching comes loose. Such defects can damage the back edge of sheets or crumple and jam sheets that are stopped by the front guides.

REMEDY: Put on new tapes.

Cause E: Rust or moisture on the feed table.

REMEDY: Keep feed table absolutely clean.

Cause F: Front edge or corners of the sheets curl up and fail to enter the side guide causing them to cock and jam.

REMEDY: Repile the sheets, rolling down the front edge and corners.

5. Front Register Varies from Sheet to Sheet

Cause A: Not enough clearance under the hold-down springs or fingers.

REMEDY: When running thin papers, adjust the clearance with a feeler gage to just twice the thickness of the paper being run. For papers over .010″ thick, adjust the clearance to 1½ times the paper thickness.

Cause B: Too much clearance under the hold-down springs or fingers. This may allow the sheets to buckle or bounce back from the stops.

REMEDY: Adjust the clearance, same as for Cause A.

Cause C: Tail-end wheels too far back or too far forward.

REMEDY: Reset tail-end wheels for proper position just off the tail end of sheets.

Cause D: Tail end of sheets not perfectly straight, or sheets varying in length from front to back. Results the same as if tail-end wheels were not properly set.

REMEDY: Retrim the stock.

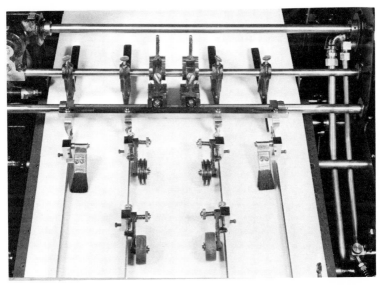

Courtesy of Harris-Seybold Co.

Figure 18.   Stream Feeder, Showing Tail-end Wheels and Brushes

Cause E: Not enough tension in the impression cylinder grippers. Tack of the ink is causing sheets to slip in the grippers with resulting misregister.

REMEDY: Check the grippers for uniform tension. Increase the tension if necessary. If the paper is very slick, glue pieces of sand- or emery paper underneath the tips of the grippers.

Cause F: Gripper edge of paper is convex or concave. This does no harm in a 3-point register system. But with multiple front guides, it can cause parts of the gripper edge to buckle, or the sheets to be gripped at slightly different angles, resulting in front-edge misregister and possibly creasing.

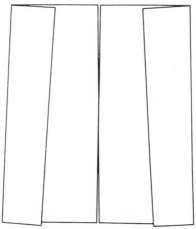

Figure 19.   Checking Straightness of Gripper Edges of Sheets

REMEDIES: Check the straightness of the gripper edge trim of the paper. If it is convex, drop some of the center stops back enough to clear the edge. If it is concave, drop the end stops back. However, since the gripper edge trim may vary from one part of the load to another, it is better to retrim the stock, if possible, to insure straightness. See LTF Publication No. 308, "What the Lithographer Should Know About Paper," page 26.

Cause G: Lack of synchronization of grippers on swing or rotary feed mechanism with impression cylinder grippers. This may be due to wear of the device that positions the gripper bar of the inserter in relation to the cylinder grippers at the instant of transfer.

REMEDY: Replace worn parts.

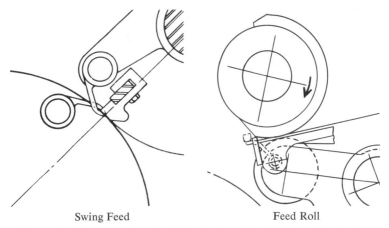

| Swing Feed | Feed Roll |

Figure 20.   Diagrams Showing Swing-feed and Feed-roll Insertion Systems

Cause H: Improper overfeed by a feed-roll mechanism.

REMEDY: Adjust timing of the feed-roll to buckle the sheets slightly as they are pushed into the gripper openings and against the cylinder stops. The amount of overfeed may change if the press speed is changed.

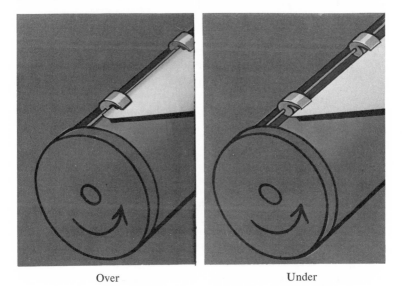

| Over | Under |

Figure 21.   Diagram Showing Over-feed (correct) and Underfeed (incorrect) in Feed-roll System

6. Side Guiding Varies from Sheet to Sheet
—Push Type Side Guides

Cause A: The pusher plate is not parallel to the edge of the sheet. This can cause variable buckling of the guide edge and result in uneven side register.

REMEDY: Adjust the alignment of the pusher plate. If worn, have the side guide mechanism repaired.

Cause B: Too much or too little clearance between the antibuckle plate and the sheet.

REMEDY: Set the anti-buckle plate with a feeler gage to give a clearance of about twice the thickness of the stock being printed.

Cause C: Side guide contacts the sheet before it has come to rest against the front guides.

REMEDY: Check and adjust the timing of both side guide and slow-down. The slow-down may be preventing the sheets from reaching the front guides in time.

Cause D: Side guide contacts the sheet after grippers have closed or sheet has started forward.

REMEDY: Correct the timing of the side guide.

7. Side Guiding Varies From Sheet to Sheet
—Pull Type Side Guide

Cause A: Pressure between the upper and lower guide rollers is too light or too heavy. Too light a pressure will fail to pull all sheets firmly up to the stop and cause irregular side register. Too much pressure will jam the edge of the sheet against the stop hard enough to buckle it with similar results.

REMEDY: Find the correct pressure for the stock being printed by making trial settings. The thinner the paper, the more critical the pressure.

Cause B: Too little clearance for the sheet at the front guides, or any other obstruction that interferes with its side movement.

REMEDY: Adjust clearance under the hold-down springs or fingers, and find and remove any obstruction to easy side movement of the sheets.

8. Gripper Edges of Sheets are Nicked or Torn

Cause A: Too much gripper bite due to improper adjustment of the front guides.

REMEDY: Set front guides back to reduce the gripper bite.

Cause B: Front guides fail to clear the edge of the sheet as it starts forward. This is true regardless of the method of insertion.

REMEDY: Check and adjust timing of the front guides.

Cause C: Lack of perfect synchronization of gripper action in transferring sheets from one set of grippers to another anywhere from feeder to delivery.

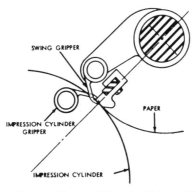

Figure 22.   Diagram Showing Transfer Gripper Timing

REMEDIES: Clean and lubricate all cams and cam rollers or followers that actuate grippers. Clean all gripper tips and pads, check gripper settings, and adjust to equal tension. Grippers should "toe" on the pads rather than "heel." If the insertion device is a feed-roll, clean and lubricate the co-acting roller under the feed board so that it turns freely, and check to see if the overfeed is correct. Check each transfer point from feeder to delivery to see that both sets of grippers firmly grip the sheet for about one-fourth inch of travel, and that the opening gripper gets out of the way without damaging the edge of the sheet. If the delivery bar grippers are not perfectly aligned with the impression cylinder grippers, move one of the chains backward or forward by shifting one of the sprockets on the skeleton cylinder. Equalize the bite between the two sets of grippers by shifting the gear that drives the skeleton cylinder. Adjust the tension on the delivery chains to eliminate slack that might affect timing of the delivery bar grippers.

9. Sheets are Wrinkled or Creased

Cause A: Paper is not flat but has wavy or tight edges.

REMEDY: Secure flat paper. See Section 7, "Paper Troubles," page 65.

Cause B: Paper slips or is pulled out of one or more grippers while being held firmly by the others. This could happen in any set of impression or transfer cylinder grippers.

REMEDY: Check all impression and transfer cylinder grippers and adjust to uniform tension.

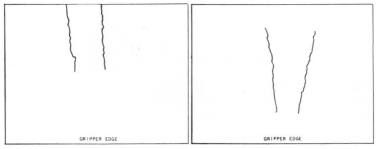

GRIPPER EDGE   GRIPPER EDGE

Figure 23.   Position of Wavy-edge   Figure 24.   Position of Tight-edge
             Wrinkle   Wrinkle

Cause C: Tumbler grippers do not all close at the same time, causing sheet distortion.

REMEDY: Readjust grippers to equal pull with strips of paper. Check shaft bearings, tumbler heads and pins, and replace if worn. Keep bearings well lubricated and gripper tips flat.

Cause D: Multiple front guides are out of line. Result is the same as if paper has a bowed gripper edge. (See 5-C above)

REMEDY: Correct front guide alignment.

10. Sheets Pull Out of Grippers and Stick to the Blanket

Cause A: Tension on the grippers is too weak to hold the paper against the pull of the ink. This is most likely to happen in printing large areas of solids. If the gripper tension is uneven, the sheets are pulled out of some grippers and torn.

REMEDY: Check the grippers for uniform tension and increase the tension if necessary. If the paper is very slick, glue pieces of sand- or emery paper underneath the tips of the grippers.

Cause B: The ink is more tacky than necessary.

REMEDY: Reduce the ink's tack. See Section 8, "Ink Troubles," page 88.

11. Printed Sheets are Being Marked or Smeared

Cause: Skeleton wheels picking up wet ink from the sheets.

REMEDY: Move skeleton wheels to margins or light areas. If there are no such areas, tie strips of sandpaper or coarse emery cloth to the skeleton wheels causing the trouble.

12. Delivered Sheets Fail to Jog Neatly

Cause A: The press moisture is expanding the printed side, causing the sheet to curl downward. Sometimes thin sheets will roll up like mailing tubes.

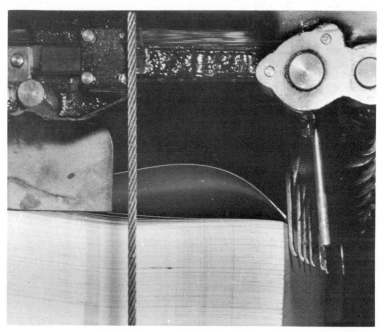

Figure 25.   Sheet Curling on Delivery

REMEDY: Reduce the plate moisture as much as possible. If this does not solve the problem, the paper is unsuitable for offset. This is a paper problem. See Section 7, page 78, and LTF Publication No. 308, "What the Lithographer Should Know About Paper," page 80.

Cause B: Printed sheets have a tail end hook so the the rear jogger is ineffective. This results when heavy solids are printed near their back edge.

REMEDIES: Reduce the tack of the ink printing the solids as much as possible. Reduce the back-cylinder pressure to a minimum. Try to avoid layouts having solids near the back edge.

Cause C: Sheets fall short of the front stops or gate, or tend to strike them too hard and buckle under.

REMEDY: Adjust the cam that controls the sheet release while the press is running at normal speed. If the press has slow-down fingers this adjustment is not critical since the fingers will place the sheet properly.

Cause D: Rear vacuum rollers may be plugged with spray powder and not controlling the sheets.

REMEDY: Clean out the vacuum rollers.

Section 2

Printing Unit Troubles

The offset press printing unit consists of a plate cylinder, blanket cylinder, and impression cylinder. These are geared together in a precise one-to-one speed ratio. Multicolor presses may consist of two or more printing units in tandem, or two or more plate and blanket cylinder couples arranged around a common impression cylinder. In some perfecting presses, the impression cylinder is omitted, the blanket cylinder of each couple acting as the impression cylinder for the other.

Proper functioning of the printing unit depends on precise meshing of driving gears and packing of the plate and blanket. Bearers are provided on American-built presses that enable accurate cylinder alignment and precise gaging of the height or radius of the plate and blanket while maintaining the gears in perfect mesh. Eu-

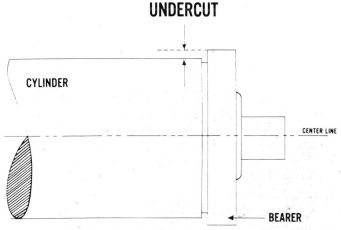

Figure 26. Diagram Showing Cylinder Body, Bearer and Undercut

23

Figure 27. Plate Cylinder, Showing Gap

ropean presses generally have no bearers and their cylinder alignment and spacing is adjusted by means of feeler gages. Plates
and blankets are packed according to prescribed micrometer
measurements. Each press manufacturer specifies the normal conditions for his presses and these should be followed. However,
there is considerable tolerance in packing the plate and blanket.
Packing sheets may be shifted from plate to blanket or vice versa,
without changing the impression pressure, to lengthen or shorten
the print when required to maintain register.

It is all important that the press cylinders be true and free from
low spots. These could be caused by warpage, or by a rag, wad of
paper, chip of wood, screw, nail, or wrench going through the
press. Damaged cylinders cannot function properly and should be
repaired.

The principal troubles due to malfunctioning of the offset printing unit with their causes and remedies are as follows:

Figure 28. Blanket Cylinder, Showing Gap

1. Gear Streaks

Gear streaks in printing are always parallel to the gripper edge of the sheets. Also, their pitch or distance apart is uniform and the same as the pitch of the teeth of the cylinder's driving gear.

Cause A: Improper packing of plate and blanket. The blanket is trying to drive the plate cylinder, in other words, fighting the gears. The trouble is worse if there is not enough bearer pressure, or if the gear teeth are worn, or if there is too much backlash.

REMEDY: Correct the plate and blanket packing. Where there is more than one printing, start color jobs with the plate over-packed and the blanket at or below bearer height. This allows more leeway for shifting packing to lengthen succeeding impressions without the blanket trying to drive the plate cylinder.

Cause B: Lack of proper bearer pressure.

REMEDY: Set bearer pressure as follows:

1. Pack plate and blanket to printing height.
2. Rub a thin film of ink on the bearers of one cylinder.
3. Place sheet of paper about .005" thick between the plate and blanket.
4. With the pressure on, turn the cylinder one revolution and inspect the bearers.
5. If there is little or no ink transfer, adjust the blanket cylinder up until there is good ink transfer at both ends.

Cause C: Too much backlash.

REMEDY: Adjust the clearance or backlash of the gears according to press manufacturer's instructions.

Cause D: Bottoming of gear teeth due to accumulation of fibers and dirt.

REMEDY: Clean the gear teeth.

Cause E: Worn cylinder bearings.

REMEDY: If remedies for A, B, C and D do not help, have the worn bearings replaced.

2. Non-Gear Streaks

Streaks other than gear streaks may be parallel to the gripper edge or from front to back. If parallel, they bear no relation to the pitch of the gear teeth.

Causes: Non-gear streaks may be caused by malfunctioning of ink rollers or dampening rollers, or by a slipping blanket.

REMEDIES: See Section 3, page 34, and Section 6, page 64.

3. Uneven Impression

Uneven color can result from two conditions—uneven or varying ink feed, and uneven cylinder pressures. Ink feeding troubles are covered in Section E. The causes of uneven pressures are as follows:

Cause A: Plate cylinder is dented or warped. To check this, proceed as follows:

1. Remove the plate and packing.
2. Run the press with a thin film of ink on the rollers and lower the best form roller until it just contacts the highest parts of the cylinder surface. Note the depressed area or spots.

REMEDY: Build up the depressed area or spots with tissue patches and shellac. Use a fine sandpaper on a flat block to taper the edges and smooth down any high spots after the shellac has dried. If the depressions are serious or the cylinder is badly warped, it should be built up by metal spraying and reground.

Cause B: The blanket is not uniform in thickness. To check this, use the LTF Thickness Gauge—by rolling the blanket in the throat of the gauge, all areas can be reached. As an alternative, proceed as follows:

1. Be sure that the plate cylinder is true (see Cause A).
2. Put on a plate and pack it to exactly bearer height.
3. Pack the blanket to .001 inch above bearers.
4. Ink up the dry plate and pull an impression on the blanket; note the bare areas.
5. Turn the blanket end for end, wash it clean and pull another ink impression on it. If the bare areas are now in different places, the blanket is at fault.

REMEDY: Patch the back of the blanket in the low areas with tissues torn to the required shape, using gum arabic. Or, if the blanket shows a bad "smash," replace it with a new one.

Cause C: The blanket was uniform in thickness when miked, but doesn't stretch and thin out uniformly when tightened on the cylinder. As a result, the center prints lighter than the side edges.

REMEDY: Punch the screw holes along one end of the blanket in a bowed line instead of straight line. This increases the tension along the sides. See GATF Publication No. 505/6, "Offset Press Operating", Pages 92-97.

Cause D: The blanket cylinder is dented or warped. To check this, first be sure that the plate cylinder is true (see Cause A), and then put a new blanket on the blanket cylinder. Follow the procedure under Cause B through item 4. If the bare area remains in the same place after the blanket has been reversed, the blanket cylinder is dented or warped.

REMEDY: If the dent is not too deep, build it up with patches of tissue torn to the required shape and applied with shellac. Use fine sandpaper on a flat block to taper the edges and smooth down any high spots after the shellac has dried.

If the dent is serious or the cylinder is warped, it should be built up by metal spraying and reground.

Cause E: The impression cylinder is dented or warped. To check this, first be sure that the plate and blanket cylinders are true and that the blanket is free from low spots (see Causes A, B and C). Then roll up the blanket with a thin film of ink and bring up the impression cylinder a little at a time until ink just begins to transfer. Transfer of ink to the impression cylinder will show up any depressions in it.

REMEDY: A dented or warped impression cylinder should be built up by metal spraying and reground.

Cause F: Plate and blanket cylinders not parallel, or blanket and impression cylinders not parallel.

REMEDY: Check press operating manual or call service man to parallel the cylinders.

Cause G: Dirty cylinder bearers. Dirt on one bearer lifts that end of the cylinder causing less pressure.

REMEDY: Keep bearers clean at all times.

Cause H: Stripping of ink rollers. This trouble is due to the rollers becoming desensitized.

REMEDY: See Section 3, page 36.

4. Slur in Halftones and at the Back Edge of Solids

Cause A: Too much back-cylinder pressure in printing on coated papers. Slur shows up on shadow tones causing loss of detail and filling in. Highlights usually are unaffected.

REMEDY: Run with a minimum of back-cylinder pressure. Run strong ink as spare as possible.

Cause B: Too much plate-to-blanket pressure when running smooth or ungrained plates.

REMEDY: Reduce plate-to-blanket squeeze to a minimum. Ungrained plates need no more than about .002 inch of impression.

Cause C: Running too much ink on coated stock.

REMEDY: Reduce ink feed. If this reduces color or black density, reduce the water feed. If necessary, use small amount of wetting agent in the fountain solution to reduce the amount required. The less the plate moisture, the less ink is required to give the desired coverage. If necessary, get a stronger ink and run less of it.

Cause D: Rippling of sheets as they enter the impression nip causing premature contact with the blanket in some areas. This can occur if the paper is not flat.

REMEDY 1: Tighten the paper hold-down brush on the compression cylinder. This applies to single-color presses and the first unit of multicolor presses. On the later units of a multicolor press, it may be necessary to use the hold-down air blasts.

Figure 30.   Blow-ups Showing Slur in a Halftone (A) Normal Print
(B) Unusually Bad Slur (C) Same Area as A but with Slur in Shadow-tone

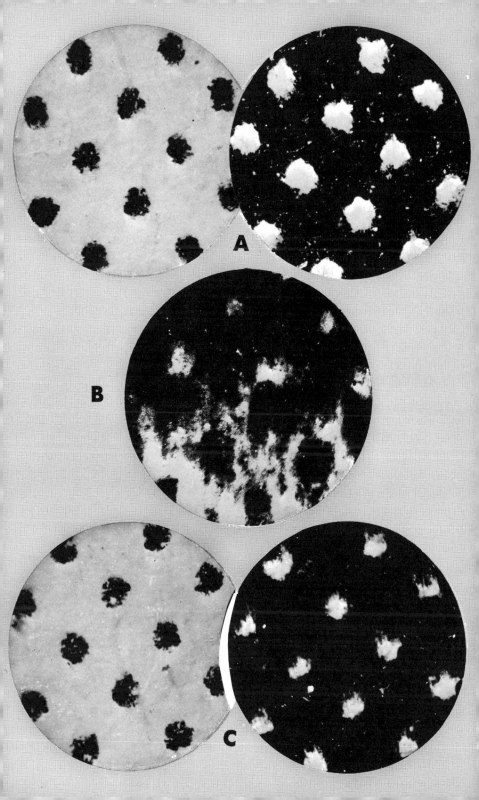

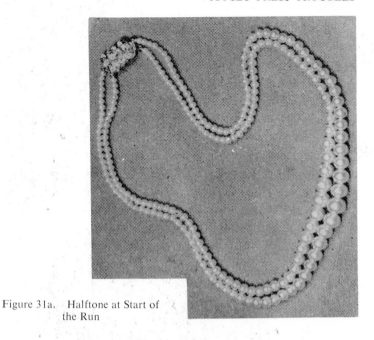

Figure 31a. Halftone at Start of the Run

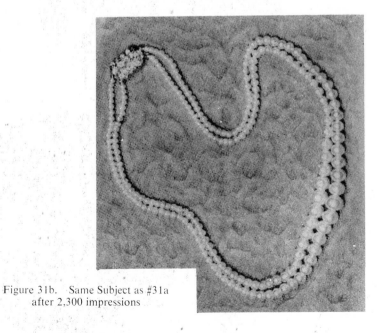

Figure 31b. Same Subject as #31a after 2,300 impressions

REMEDY 2: Recondition the paper to reduce waviness or tight edges.

Note: Causes A, B, and C usually produce slurring over the entire sheet. Causes D and E produce slurring in some areas, not in others.

Cause E: Piling of paper coating on the printing areas of the blanket. This usually starts in the middle halftones on the second or a later unit of a multicolor press, producing a mottled pattern due to slurred dots.

REMEDY: Switch to a more moisture-resistant coated stock. See Section 7, page 81.

5. Doubling on Multicolor Presses

On multicolor presses, the first-down ink image is transferred from the sheet onto non-image areas of the blanket of the second unit; the second-down ink image transfers to the blanket of the third unit, and so on. These images print back onto the following sheets. Unless this print-back is in exact register with the original print, a double is produced. Doubling is particularly objectionable

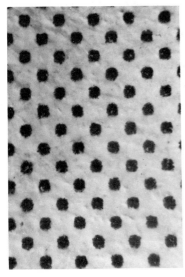

Figure 32a.   Blow-up of Normal Halftone

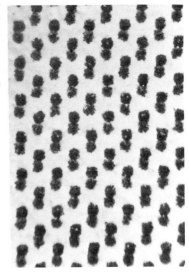

Figure 32b.   Same Halftone as 32a but with Double

in halftones since it varies from sheet to sheet causing up-and-down variations in color values. There are three possible causes of doubling.

Cause A: Sheets slipping in grippers. If a sheet slips slightly in the grippers, the print-back from the following blanket is out of register causing a double and increasing the color value. Such slippage varies from sheet to sheet causing variations in color values.

REMEDY 1: Adjust impression and transfer cylinder grippers, making sure that tension is sufficient and uniform.

REMEDY 2: Try reducing tne ink's ʈack on the unit where slippage is occurring. This unit is likely to be the one printing the largest solid areas.

Cause B: Play in impression or transfer cylinders. Can be either end play, or play due to backlash, tortional flexing, or worn bearings.

REMEDY: Set backlash to a minimum. If this does not remove the trouble, have the press overhauled and worn parts replaced.

Cause C: Paper being distorted in the impression due to its being wavy-edged or tight-edged. Unfortunately, no unflat sheet will be distorted in exactly the same way in successive impressions. And no two such sheets will be distorted in the same way by the same printing unit. As a result, the pick-up of all but the final color will vary in position on the succeeding blankets, producing doubles and variable halftone color values.

REMEDY: The use of reasonably flat paper. Paper that is slightly tight-edged gives less trouble than stock that is wavy-edged. (See Section 7, "Paper Troubles" pages 67–69.)

Section 3

Ink Feed and Distribution Troubles

The inking system for each offset printing unit usually consists of an ink fountain, fountain roller, ductor roller, three or four metal oscillating (vibrating) drums, four or more rubber intermediate rollers, and three or four rubber or vulcanized oil composition form rollers. The ink fountain and ductor roller cooperate to feed the ink in controlled amounts. The drums and rollers distribute it to a more or less uniform thin film and work it into printing consistency. The form rollers then apply the ink to the plate image according to its requirements.

In order to function properly, the oscillating drums must be driven by gears or chains and must have the same surface speed as the printing plate. The ductor, intermediate and form rollers are driven by surface contact only. The fountain roller is driven intermittently by means of an adjustable pawl and ratchet. The setting of the fountain blade and the movement of the fountain roller determine the amount of ink delivered to the rollers and eventually to the printed sheets.

Uniform distribution of ink around the rollers results from the rollers and drums having different diameters. Distribution lengthwise of the rollers is produced by oscillation of the vibrating drums which is usually adjustable. Ink film thickness lengthwise of the rollers is not necessarily uniform since the requirements of the form may vary considerably across the press. Such local requirements are met by adjusting the flexible fountain blade.

The principle troubles that can be attributed to the inking system are as follows:

33

1. Horizontal Streaks in the Printing— Other than Gear Streaks

Roller streaks are always parallel to the gripper edge of the sheets. But unlike gear streaks they have no relationship to the pitch of the teeth of the cylinder drive gear. There may be only one streak or several. They may or may not be spaced at equal distances.

Cause A: One or more form rollers set too hard against the plate. They strike the leading edge of the plate and bounce. This ruptures their ink film from end to end producing a streak on the roller which is transferred to the plate after one revolution. Such streaks are worse if all form rollers are the same size and all are set too hard against the plate. They are most objectionable on background color tints.

REMEDY: Reset the form rollers to proper pressures against the plate and drum. (See LTF Publication No. 505/6, "Lithographic Offset Press Operating," page 36, and LTF Audio Visual #5, "Inking and Dampening Systems.")

Cause B: Too much end play in form rollers which permits them to move endwise with the oscillating drums. If the form rollers are on the plate when the drum movement reverses, they may slip endwise and produce streaks.

REMEDY 1: Adjust form roller sockets to eliminate end play. If necessary, place washers on the roller spindles.

Figure 33. Strip Method of Roller Setting: Picture on Plate
Showing Roller Setting

REMEDY 2: On some presses the timing of drum oscillation can be adjusted so that the reversal in direction can be made to occur while the form rollers are opposite the plate cylinder gap. This should eliminate streaks caused by end play.

Cause C: Skidding form rollers. This can be caused by a roller being set with unequal pressure against its drum and the plate. The harder the setting, the greater the driving force and the slower the form roller is driven. So, if settings are unequal, the roller will skid on the surface where the setting is lighter and produce streaks. Skidding is more likely to occur if the rollers are glazed.

REMEDY 1: Reset the form rollers with equal pressures against the drums and plate.

REMEDY 2: Recondition the form rollers and drums to remove glaze. Glaze is due to accumulations of dried ink vehicle and gum not removed by ordinary wash-up solvents. Use one of the newer glaze removing wash-up materials. Alternatively, remove the form rollers, and scrub them and the drums with pumice powder and solvent to remove the glaze.

Cause D: A loose and slipping blanket. Because it is frequently necessary to lengthen or shorten the print, the surface speed of the plate and blanket are not always exactly equal. If the blanket is loose, it may tend to follow the plate and slip on the blanket cylinder. This slippage is intermittent, causing streaks. The greater the plate-to-blanket pressure, the worse the slippage.

REMEDY: Tighten the blanket. Use the packing gage to check the plate-to-blanket pressure and, if too high, remove the excess packing.

Cause E: Worn or mismatched drive belts. If one belt becomes frayed or stretches more than the other(s), the resulting uneven surges of power can cause streaks.

REMEDY: Replace with a complete set of matched belts.

2. Ink Feeds Unevenly

Ink is fed by intermittent rotation of the fountain roller. The amount is controlled by (1) setting of the flexible fountain blade by which the amount of ink can be varied across the press according to the demands of the plate; and (2) the rotation of the fountain roller which can be varied, and which governs the amount of ink fed to all areas.

The ductor roller alternately contacts the fountain roller and the upper ink drum. It transfers fresh ink to the drum in the form of a streak which is then worked out to a smooth film by the time it reaches the form rollers. The lateral vibration (oscillation) of the drums tends to spread the ink uniformly sidewise across the press. However, it is generally adjustable so that a differential ink feed to areas of greater or lesser demand can be maintained. Lateral distribution is reduced to a minimum when operating with two or more colors in a split fountain.

Ink feeding and distribution troubles can arise from a number of causes:

Cause A: Stripping of ink drums or rollers. This can result from: (a) glazed rollers; (b) running too much dampening solution; or (c) using too much gum or phosphoric acid or both in the dampening solution. In any case, the rollers become desensitized and preferentially wet by water, and refuse to take or transfer ink. The result is inability to maintain color. Generally, it is the metal drums that strip but if rubber and vulcanized oil rollers become glazed they too can strip.

REMEDY 1: Wash up the press by using one of the newer glaze removing wash-up methods.

Figure 34.   Stripping of Steel Ink Drum

REMEDY 2: If only the metal drums are stripping, wash the system free from ink, remove the form and intermediate rollers, and scrub the metal drums thoroughly with pumice powder and solvent.

REMEDY 3: If rubber or vulcanized oil rollers strip, the glaze can be removed by scrubbing them with a 5% caustic soda solution and pumice powder. (Caution: for this job, wear goggles, rubber gloves and a rubber apron). Alternatively, these rollers can be reground in a lathe to remove the glaze.

REMEDY 4: Since the metal drums are the principal cause of stripping trouble, these can be removed and covered with Ebonite or electroplated with copper. Both materials strongly resist stripping.

REMEDY 5: To avoid removing the metal drums, which involves partially tearing down the press, they can be chemically copperized on the press by means of LTF's Copper Plating Solution for Steel Ink Rollers (see LTF Publications No. 602, 805 or 806). This copper plating is very thin and may wear off in from a week to six months, but it is easily renewed.

Cause B: Ink "backs away" from the fountain roller causing its feed to diminish. Actually, the ink does not back away—it simply sets up in the fountain and refuses to flow down to the fountain roller. Such an ink may be too short, too thixotropic (see LTF Publication No. 310), or too cold.

REMEDY 1: Work the ink in the fountain frequently to keep it fluid.

Figure 35. Ink Fountain Agitator

REMEDY 2: Install a mechanical ink fountain agitator.

REMEDY 3: Obtain a longer, more fluid ink.

REMEDY 4: Raise the pressroom temperature. Most inks work best at 75° to 80° F.

Cause C: Ink builds, cakes or piles on the roller surfaces and on the image areas of the plate and blanket. When this happens the ink fails to transfer properly, resulting in loss of color. Piling may be due to incompletely dispersed pigment, or to the ink becoming waterlogged.

REMEDY 1: Check the degree of dispersion of pigments in the ink by means of the Fineness-of-Grind Gage or Grindometer (see LTF Publication No. 310). If the test shows many coarse particles or aggregates, have the ink reground.

REMEDY 2: Reduce the plate moisture to a minimum. If this does not help, try adding a small amount of water-resistant varnish to the ink, or get an ink that resists waterlogging.

Cause D: The ink rollers become fouled with lint from the paper. Lint, being cellulose fiber, absorbs water and becomes ink repellent, and refuses to transfer a continuous ink film.

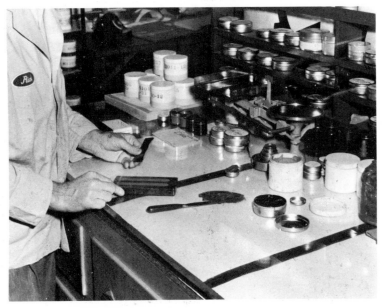

Figure 36.   Using Ink Fineness-of-Grind Gage

REMEDY 1: Wash all possible ink off the rollers with the wash-up attachment. Then hand wash the rollers and drums to remove the lint. Reduce tack of the ink.

REMEDY 2: Obtain paper that has a minimum linting tendency.

Cause E: Low spots in rollers preventing uniform contact between them or between form rollers and plate. The rubber or vulcanized oil rollers are the most likely to have low spots.

Remedy: Remove the defective rollers and have them reground, taking off enough material to render them absolutely true.

Cause F: Roller cores or spindles are bent.

REMEDY: Remove the defective rollers and have their coverings removed. Have the cores or spindles trued up and re-covered.

Cause G: The fountain blade has become bent or has worn unevenly and developed a scalloped edge. This prevents accurate setting.

REMEDY: Obtain a new, straight fountain blade. When installing it, be sure that the screws are backed off and that they turn freely. Use the screws and a feeler gage to adjust the blade according to the press manufacturer's instructions, usually to a clearance of .050 inch. From this point, make further adjustments according to job requirements. Never force the blade against the fountain roller since this would cause uneven wear. When tightening the blade over-all, start by turning the screws at the center and work toward the ends. When opening up the blade gap, start at both ends and work toward the center. This will tend to prevent the development of a buckle or kink in the blade.

Cause H: Dirt or dried ink has accumulated between the fountain blade and roller, interfering with the ink feed.

REMEDY: Keep the blade and roller clean at all times.

Cause I: The ends of rubber form rollers blister, swell or peel. The ends of vulcanized oil rollers crack and begin to break up. The result is poor inking along the sides of the plate. This is due to the wash-up attachment leaving ink and solvent to dry on the ends of the rollers.

REMEDY: When the machine wash-up is completed, always wipe the ends of the rollers and drums dry. Rollers that have become damaged should be replaced.

Section 4

Plate Dampening Troubles

Most offset presses are equipped with the conventional dampening system consisting of water pan or fountain, fountain roller, ductor roller, distributing roller (vibrator) and two form dampening rollers.

The fountain roller is partly immersed in the fountain solution and rotates slowly. On many presses its speed varies with the press speed, but the present trend is toward an independent variable speed drive. It is of rust-resisting metal and may either be bare or covered with a muslin sleeve.

The conventional ductor roller is a molleton or Aquatex covered roller that runs in contact alternately with the fountain roller and distributing roller. Its dwell on the fountain roller is adjustable and, if the speed of the fountain roller varies with the press speed, controls the amount of moisture fed to the dampening rollers. If the fountain roller has a variable-speed drive, this also controls the water feed and makes possible finer adjustments.

The water distributing roller formerly was brass. But, since brass is hard to desensitize to ink, it is now generally made of aluminum or stainless steel. This roller is driven so that its surface speed is the same as that of the pressplate when packed to the specified height.

For many years there was only one type of form dampening roller. It consisted of a steel core which carried a sleeve of coarse wool flannel and on top of that a sleeve of molleton or Aquatex. The first important change was the use of a rubber covered core and omission of the flannel underlayer. The next important change was the use of a parchment paper strip wound spirally on existing dampening rollers. This was followed by omission of the fabric cover and winding the parchment directly on a special rubber roller. Parchment paper covers are easily replaceable and can be changed daily, if necessary. Each of these developments has brought about an improvement. Many pressmen now run with only one parchment paper dampening roller on the plate instead of two.

The reason for all these developments has been the need for more precise control of the amount and distribution of the plate moisture. But they would not have been possible except for improvements in printing plates, namely, finer grains or no grain at all, and better desensitization.

Developments are still taking place. There is the Effusor dampening system in which more than enough water is applied to the plate and the excess blown off with an air knife. More generally accepted is the Dahlgren system in which the dampening solution can contain 25 percent of alcohol and is applied to the first form ink roller instead of to the plate. These systems have made it possible to lithograph on some letterpress coated papers formerly considered unsuitable.

Another recent development is the brush ductor that runs in constant contact with the fountain roller and "flips" moisture from it to the metal distributing roller. Here the variable speed of the fountain roller alone controls the amount of moisture supplied.

Proper plate dampening is essential to control of the ink-water balance which, in turn, is essential to high quality offset printing. And the following press troubles can result when it is not accomplished.

1. Wash Marks

These appear as weak areas extending back from the leading edges of solids.

Figure 37.   Wash Marks in Solid Caused by Excessive Dampening

Cause: Too much dampening water, and the excess is not being taken up by the ink.

REMEDY: Reduce the water feed. But if the water control is so critical as to leave little margin between wash marks and scumming, either the plate is too poorly desensitized or the ink is too water-repellent.

2. Snowflaky Solids

Black solids are gray and color solids are weak. Under a glass they appear uneven and full of tiny white specks.

Cause: Too much dampening water, the excess being taken up by the ink. Then, when the ink film is split, water droplets are exposed. These prevent transfer of a uniform solid to the paper.

REMEDY: Reduce the water feed (see also remedy for (1) above). If the ink on the rollers appears to be waterlogged (greatly shortened by the moisture), change to an ink that is resistant to waterlogging.

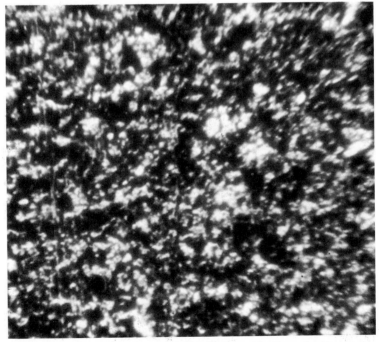

Figure 38.   Blow-up of "Snow-Flaky" Solid Caused by Excessive Dampening

3. Color Varies With No Change in Ink Feed

This can be caused by stripping of ink rollers, ink "backing away" from the fountain roller or piling on the ink rollers, fouling of the ink by paper lint and dust, low spots in rollers, bent roller cores or spindles, or dirt or dried ink between the fountain blade and roller (see Section 3). If none of these causes apply, consider the following:

Cause: Variation in feed of the dampening solution.

REMEDY: Maintain a constant level of solution in the water fountain. Water fountain levelers are available for this purpose.

4. Scum Streaks Appear in the Round-the-Cylinder Direction

Scum streaks are usually due to lack of sufficient moisture or to excessive plate wear.

Cause A: Dirty or worn dampener or ductor roller covers, or greasing of the fountain roller or distributing roller. These conditions can prevent uniform dampening across the press.

REMEDY: If the dampener or ductor roller covers have become dirty, wash them to remove ink accumulations. If they have become threadbare, replace them. If the fountain and distributing rollers have become greasy and fail to hold continuous films of water, scrub them with powdered pumice and naptha, then etch them, drying the etch down.

Cause B: Non-uniform pressure of dampening rollers against the plate causing uneven wear.

REMEDY 1: Reset dampening rollers, making sure the pressure is uniform from end to end. After setting, make sure they are never reversed.

REMEDY 2: Check dampeners for trueness. If a spindle or stock is bent, it should be straightened and the roller re-covered.

5. Scum Streaks Appear Across the Plate

These are also usually due to lack of sufficient moisture or to excessive plate wear.

Cause A: Bouncing dampening rollers. Rollers are set too hard against the plate. When they strike the leading edge of the plate they bounce. The bump causes rapid wear of the plate's front edge, producing a scum streak. It also squeezes an excess of moisture onto the plate in a line from end to end of the dampeners. This in turn causes a water streak just one revolution of the roller back from the leading edge.

REMEDY: Reset the dampening rollers to the proper pressure to eliminate bounce. (For other causes of scum streaks across the plate, see Section 3, page 34).

6. The Plate Tends to Scum Generally after 10–20,000 Impressions

Cause: This trouble may be due to insufficient acid or gum or both in the fountain solution.

REMEDY: Add enough fountain etch to bring the pH value of the fountain solution down to 4.5–5.5. Use pH control consistently. (See LTF Publication No. 803, "pH, What it is, How to measure it, Where to use it").

(For other causes of plate scumming, see Section 5, page 52).

Figure 39.   Testing Fountain Solution with Portable pH Meter

7. Halftones Sharpen and Highlight Dots are Lost During Run

Cause: Too much acid in the fountain solution is undermining the work areas.

REMEDY: Once highlight dots have been lost, they cannot be brought back. Have the plate remade, and adjust the pH value of the fountain solution to 4.5–5.5.
(For other causes of image failure, see Section 5, page 56).

8. Fiber-Shaped White Spots Appear in Printed Solids

Fiber-shaped spots are the result of cellulose fibers adhering to either the plate or the blanket. Such fibers absorb moisture until they become saturated after which they repel ink and print reverse images of themselves.

Cause A: Lint, fluff or whiskers being picked up from the paper or board. This is a paper trouble.

REMEDY: (See Section 7, page 74).

Cause B: Fibers released from molleton or Aquatex dampening roller covers. These covers eventually begin to shed their nap fibers as a result of wear or possibly mildew. They can be distinguished from paper fibers since they are generally from two to four times as long. They can also be identified by laboratory tests (TAPPI Standard No. T 401 M).

REMEDY 1: Re-cover the dampener and ductor rollers.

REMEDY 2: Use parchment paper dampener covers. These are replaced frequently and do not shed fibers.

REMEDY 3: Install one of the newer dampening systems that do not require roller covers (see pages 40–41).

9. The Plate Image Thickens During the Run

(See Section 5, pages 52–55)

10. The Plate Image Sharpens

(See Section 5, pages 56–59)

11. The Plate Image Wears or Goes Blind

(See Section 5, page 56)

12. The Plate Scums or Tints

(See Section 5, pages 52–56)

13. Paper Curls on Delivery

(See Section 7, page 78)

14. Ink Chalks

(See Section 8, page 93)

15. Ink Fails to Dry on Schedule

(See Section 8, pages 91–93)

Section 5

Press Plate Troubles

The lithographic press plate is different from other mechanical printing plates in that it is planographic. This means that its image and non-image areas are essentially on the same level. The image areas are not raised as in letterpress, nor depressed as in gravure printing. They are simply ink-receptive areas surrounded by water-receptive areas. When moistened, the water-receptive areas refuse to take ink, while the image areas repel the water.

The printing cycle consists, therefore, in (1) dampening the plate's non-image areas, (2) inking the image areas, and (3) transferring ink from the image areas to the blanket from which it is "offset" on to the paper, paperboard, metal, plastic, or whatever surface is being printed.

On the first metal lithographic plates, the image areas were drawn by hand with crayon or tusch, or were produced by hand-transferring ink images from stones. Later it was found that the image areas could be produced photographically using negatives or positives. This greatly improved the quality of halftones, and to-day "photolithographic" methods of platemaking are used exclusively.

Many photolithographic processes have been proposed but only a few have proven practical in commercial lithography and these will be briefly described.

Surface Plates: These are made by coating a clean metal plate with a light-sensitive film, exposing to light through a line or half-tone negative, developing to remove the unexposed coating from the non-image areas, and desensitizing the non-image areas. The image areas are inked up before, during or after the development.

Figure 40.   Cross Section Diagram of Surface Plate

There are three types of surface plates: (1) grained zinc or aluminum plates sensitized with bichromated albumin or casein; (2) ungrained aluminum plates sensitized with diazo compounds, called "pre-sensitized plates," and purchased ready for exposure; (3) grained zinc or aluminum plates sensitized with diazo compounds by the lithographer, called "wipe-on" plates.

Deep-Etch Plates: These are made by coating a clean zinc, aluminum or stainless steel plate with bichromated gum arabic, exposing to light through a line of halftone positive, developing to remove unexposed coating from the image areas, "deep-etching" the image areas, applying lacquer and ink to the image areas, removing the bichromated gum stencil, and desensitizing the non-image areas.

Figure 41.   Cross Section Diagram of Deep-Etch Plate

Actually the deep-etching is less than 7 microns (0.0003 inch), too shallow to produce appreciable image depression. All that is really necessary is to remove enough metal to assure absolute cleanness.

In the case of aluminum plates, the image areas are often copperized to increase the adhesion of lacquer and ink.

For details on methods of making surface and deep-etch plates, see LTF Publications Nos. 502, 504, 804, 805, 806 and 807.

Bimetal Plates: These are distinguished by having image and non-image areas of different metals—chromium, stainless steel or aluminum for the non-image areas and copper for the image areas.

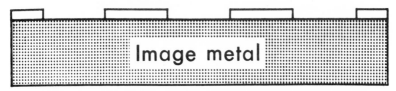

Figure 42.   Cross Section Diagram of Bimetal Plate: Negative Type

There are two general types of bimetal plates: (1) "negative-working" plates, in which copper is electroplated on stainless steel or aluminum. These are exposed through negatives, developed to bare the copper in the non-image areas, then etched to remove the copper from these areas, leaving copper on the printing areas; (2) "positive-working" plates in which copper is electroplated on a zinc, aluminum or iron base plate, followed by a thin layer of electroplated chromium. These are exposed through positives, developed to bare the chromium in the image areas, then etched to remove the chromium from the image areas, leaving chromium on the non-image areas. Such plates are often called "trimetal" plates.

Paper Plates: There are two general types of paper plates—direct-image plates upon which the image is produced by typewriting or printing, and pre-sensitized plates upon which the image is produced photographically. Such plates are used extensively on offset duplicators, but are available in commercial sizes up to about 40″ x 54″. These plates are primarily for black and white printing and are not recommended for multicolor work.

There is considerable difference in the cost of these different plates, and the length of run usually determines which one is selected. Their approximate printing life is as follows:

Type of Plate	Length of Run
Presensitized Paper Plates	up to 5,000
Direct-Image Paper Plates	up to 10,000
Presensitized Aluminum	20,000– 50,000

(*Continued on next page*)

Figure 43.   Cross Section Diagram of Bimetal Plate: Positive Type

Type of Plate	Length of Run
Wipe-On	50,000–100,000
Albumin and Casein	50,000–150,000
Zinc Deep-Etch	100,000–250,000
Copperized Aluminum Deep-Etch	300,000–500,000
Bimetal or Trimetal	1,000,000+

In any case, plate life and print quality depend both on correct plate preparation and proper plate handling on the press.

The following are the principle plate troubles likely to be encountered on the press.

1. Plate Image Under Developing Ink Cannot be Washed Out with Naptha or Lithotine

Cause A: Gum has dried over all or part of the work areas, preventing solvent from contacting and dissolving the developing ink.

REMEDY: Wash gum off the plate with water and, while wet, wash off the ink with naptha or Lithotine. Then wash the plate thoroughly with water to remove the ink solvent, and finally drop the form rollers to ink up the work areas. (For detailed instructions on wet-washing plates, see LTF Publications Nos. 804, 805, or 806).

Cause B: Developing ink has dried hard on the work areas and naptha or Lithotine will not remove it.

REMEDY 1: Wash the plate with a solvent for dried ink, such as a 50-50 mixture of xylol and ethyl acetate or butyl acetate. When the ink has been removed, put the plate under asphaltum.

REMEDY 2: Have platemaker use a developing ink that will not dry hard, or ask him to put plates under asphaltum.

2. Plate Refuses to Roll up Properly

Cause A: Gum has dried over part or all of the work, often in streaks, and has desensitized it.

REMEDY: Try wet-washing the plate and rolling it up with ink (see Cause 1-A above). If this does not help, get a new plate. Before gumming up plates, be sure they are fully inked up. For

Figure 44. Steps in Wet-Washing a Plate

(a) With the ink and dampener rollers up, wash the plate with clean water and a sponge.

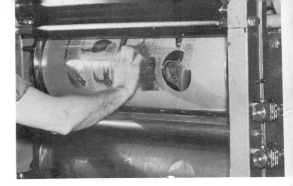

(b) While the plate is still damp with water, wash the ink off the image using a soft cloth and Lithotine solvent. Go over the plate twice with the solvent. Don't let the plate dry.

(c) Wash the solvent and dissolved ink off the plate with clean water and a sponge. Go over the plate twice.

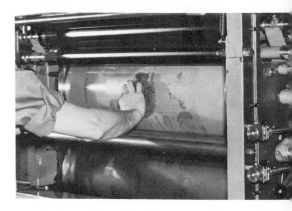

(d) While the plate is still damp with water, start the press and drop the ink rollers. When image is fully inked, drop the dampeners, and resume or start printing.

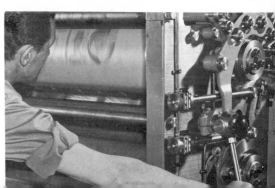

detailed instructions on gumming up plates, see LTF Publications Nos. 804, 805 or 806.

Cause B: Developing ink has dried on the work areas and cannot be washed out.

REMEDY: Same as for 1-B (above).

3. Plate Under Asphaltum Cannot be Washed Out with Water

Cause A: Asphaltum was put on so thick that water cannot penetrate it and dissolve the gum.

REMEDY: Wet-wash the plate and roll it up with ink (see Cause 1-A above). If work does not roll up properly, get a new plate. For detailed instructions on putting plates under asphaltum, see LTF Publications Nos. 804, 805 or 806.

Cause B: Too thin a gum film on the plate when asphaltum was applied, and asphaltum penetrated it.

REMEDY: Try wet-washing and rolling up the plate (see 1-A above). If this does not work, get a new plate.

Cause C: Gum on the plate was not thoroughly dry when asphaltum was applied. Asphaltum penetrated it.

REMEDY: Try wet-washing and rolling up the plate (see 1-A, above). On future plates, make sure gum is thoroughly dry.

To remove scum from bimetal plates, see notes under #8, page 58.

4. Non-Image Areas Become Greasy or Scummy

Cause A: Dirty or worn dampener covers.

REMEDY: Clean or re-cover the dampening rollers. Wet-washing may save the plate.

Cause B: Running too much ink on halftones. The ink squashes on the dots and spreads over the open areas, eventually sensitizing them.

REMEDY: Run the ink as stiff and spare as possible.

Cause C: Slurring of halftones. This causes open areas in halftones to fill in and the back edges of solids to lose sharpness. It usually results from excessive pressure or excessive ink especially in printing on coated stocks.

REMEDY: Reduce ink feed and reduce plate-to-blanket and back-cylinder pressures to a minimum. (For detailed discussions on dot slur, Section 2, page 28, and LTF Publications Nos. 804, 805, 806 or 310).

Cause D: Oxidation of zinc or aluminum plates. This happens if:

1. A wet plate dries too slowly.
2. A plate is stored in a damp area either before processing or while it is being held for a re-run.
3. The press is stopped during a run with the dampening rollers opposite a moist plate area so that drying of this area is retarded. On aluminum plates, oxidation appears as a multitude of fine, sharp dots. Scum of this type always appears in horizontal streaks.

REMEDY: The best remedy for oxidation scum is prevention —that is, care in handling zinc and aluminum plates. Always store them in a dry place. During platemaking, dry them with a fan.

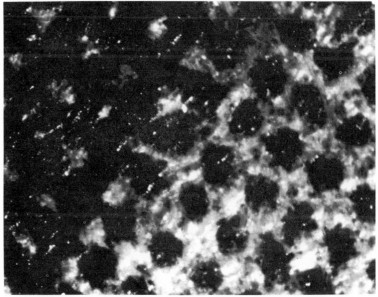

Figure 45. Blow-up Showing Oxidation (Ink-Dot) Scum Between Halftone Dots on an Aluminum Plate

When shutting down a press, allow it to idle until the plate or plates are dry. When stopped, see that the dampeners are opposite the cylinder gap. If the scum is very light, it may be possible to remove it by etching the plate. Otherwise the plate should be remade.

Cause E: Improper functioning of dampening or inking rollers, or of both, resulting in scum streaks either horizontal or around the cylinder. These troubles are not the fault of the plate.

REMEDIES: (See Section 3, page 34 and Section 4, page 44).

Cause F: Plate was not properly desensitized when made.

REMEDY: Try re-etching and gumming the plate on the press. Before doing this, be sure the image areas are well protected with ink and preferably powdered with a 50–50 mixture of powdered rosin and French chalk. Also, be sure to dry the etch down thoroughly before washing it off. If this does not remove the scum, try wet-washing the plate and rolling the image up with ink before etching and gumming it. (See items in LTF Publications Nos. 804, 805 and 806 on wet-washing plates.)

Cause G: Ink is too soft or greasy.

REMEDY: Stiffen the ink with No. 8 varnish or body gum. If this does not help, try another stiffer ink.

Cause H: Abrasive particles in the ink.

REMEDY: Have the ink reground or replace it with a better ink.

Cause I: Abrasive picked up from the paper surface by the offset blanket.

REMEDY: Reduce the plate-to-blanket and back-cylinder pressures to a minimum. If possible, change to another paper.

Cause J: "Counter-Etching in Multicolor," sometimes called "secondary scumming." This can occur on any unit of a multicolor press except the first. What happens, for example, is that printed ink from the first (yellow) unit is picked up by the offset blanket of the second (red) unit so that it runs in contact with non-image areas of the red plate. If it sensitizes these areas, they will develop a red scum that prints over the yellow areas of the sheets, changing their values. There are several possible causes.

REMEDY 1: If poor plate desensitization is suspected, re-etch and gum up the scumming plate. (See Cause F, above)

REMEDY 2: Increase the acid and gum in the fountain water on the plate giving trouble.

REMEDY 3: Run the ink sparer on the preceding unit. If necessary, mix the ink stronger.

This type of scumming is usually less troublesome the finer the plate grain. It seldom occurs when running bimetal plates.

5. Non-Image Areas Print an Over-all Tint Although Plate is not Greasy

Cause A: Fountain water is extracting an emulsifying or sensitizing agent from the paper coating. This is proved if substituting another paper stops the tinting.

REMEDY: Stiffen the ink as much as possible with No. 8 varnish or body gum or try another, stiffer ink. Avoid use of a wetting agent in the fountain water. If tinting continues, get another paper. (See Section 7, page 84).

Cause B: The non-image areas of the plate have not been well desensitized due to incomplete removal of bichromated colloid plate coating. This applies to both surface and deep-etch plates. To check this, wash all tint off the plate, polish part of a blank area with a Scotch Stone or Snakeslip, and give the entire plate a light etch. If, on resuming the run, the polished-out area remains clean while the surrounding area tints, the cause is residual coating. If all areas continue tinting, the cause is either the paper (see Cause A) or breakdown of the ink (see Cause C).

REMEDY 1: If the above test indicates the presence of residual coating, try adding more fountain etch, but do not reduce the pH value of the fountain water below about 4.5. Otherwise the ink may not dry. If this does not stop the tinting, send the plate back to the plate room for further treatment (see plate post-treatments, LTF Publications Nos. 504, 602 or 805.)

REMEDY 2: In the case of an aluminum deep-etch plate with residual coating, wash it with the following solution:

Oxalic acid	6 ounces
Hot water	1 pint

Apply with a rag or sponge, then wash off with water and proceed to print.

Cause C: The ink is not sufficiently water-resistant and is breaking down and emulsifying in the plate moisture. If, in single-color presswork, changing the paper does not stop the tinting, the trouble is with either the ink or the plate. In multicolor press work, the cause should be fairly obvious. If all the inks are tinting, the cause is most likely the paper (see Cause A). If one or two inks are tinting while the others are printing clean, ink or plate trouble is indicated.

REMEDY 1: If the test described under Cause B indicates plate trouble, try the remedy suggested there. If, however, not all of the inks tint, or changing the paper does not stop the tinting, the offending inks should either be stiffened or replaced with more water-resistant inks.

> **Note: Inks designed for large or high speed presses are likely to break down and tint when run on small presses or at low speed.**

6. Plate Fails to Print Full-Strength Color

Cause A: Image lacks ink affinity.

REMEDY: Wet-wash the plate. (See items in LTF Publications Nos. 804, 805 or 806 on wet-washing plates.)

Cause B: Ink is too short or is water-logged and is piling on the rollers, plate and blanket.

REMEDY: Lengthen the ink by adding long or water resistant varnish. Cut down fountain water to a minimum.

Cause C: Plate is starting to go blind.

REMEDY: (See No. 7, Image Goes Blind—below)

7. Image Goes Blind or "Walks Off"

Cause A: Too much gum in the fountain water.

REMEDY: Drain the water fountain and fill with plain tap water. Lift the form rollers. With dampeners on the plate, run waste sheets until ink on the plate is exhausted. Then drop the form rollers and proceed to print. This treatment removes gum sticking to the image areas. (See LTF Publication No. 806, page 96, "Bringing Back a Blind Plate.")

Cause B: Too much acid in the fountain water. This is indicated by roller stripping, or by tendency of the plate to scum prior to loss of image.

REMEDY: Drain fountain and replace solution with one having a higher pH value—preferably between 5.0 and 6.0.

Cause C: Ink is too short and lacks water resistance.

REMEDY: Rub up the image areas. Before resuming the run, add medium varnish to the ink. If necessary, mix fresh ink with less shortening compound.

Cause D: Plate-to-blanket pressure is too great. This may be due to a swollen or embossed blanket.

REMEDY: Correct the plate-to-blanket pressure. If blanket is badly embossed, replace it.

Cause E: Image lacquer is not resistant to blinding.

REMEDY: Try remedy for Cause A (above). If this does not work, try going over the plate with a rag or sponge dampened with lacquer solvent, then quickly roll up with ink. If this does not help, get a new plate. (See sections on "Non-blinding Lacquer" in LTF Publications Nos. 805 and 806).

Cause F: Deep-etch plate was not completely developed. A thin film of gum still remains on the image areas. This gum eventually takes water and releases the lacquer, and the image becomes grainy, spotty or blind.

REMEDY: None. Have the plate remade.

8. Bimetal Plate Goes Blind

Cause A: The copper image on a chromium-copper or aluminum-copper bimetal plate has become desensitized. This could be caused by an accumulation of gum in the ink, or by sulfur or a sulfur compound.

REMEDY: Rub up the image areas with ink and dilute phosphoric or nitric acid (12 ounces to a gallon of water). Wash off the acid, etch the plate, and proceed to print.

Caution: This treatment should not be used on copperized aluminum plates since chemically deposited copper is not sufficiently resistant.

Cause B: The copper image on a stainless steel-copper plate has become desensitized (see Cause A, above).

REMEDY: Rub up the image areas with ink and 2 percent sulfuric acid (2½ ounces concentrated sulfuric acid to a gallon of water). Wash off the acid, etch the plate, and proceed to print.

Caution: In making the 2 percent sulfuric acid, always add the acid to the water. Adding water to concentrated sulfuric acid could cause spattering and injury to the eyes and skin.

Note 1: Since sulfur and sulfide compounds cause blinding of copper images, never use sulfur to dust the offset blanket, or a carbon disulfide solution of sulfur to relieve blanket tackiness, when printing with copperized aluminum or bimetal plates.

Note 2: The above acid treatments not only re-sensitize the copper image areas of bimetal plates, but also remove scum from the non-image areas. However, plates should be re-etched to keep scum from coming back.

9. Halftones Print Grainy or Sandy

Cause A: Deep-etch plate not completely developed. Could be due to overexposure or dark reaction.

REMEDY: None. Have the plate remade.

Cause B: Coarse or uneven plate grain.

REMEDY: None. Have plate remade with finer grain.

Cause C: Too much fountain water. Water emulsifies in the ink and shortens or waterlogs it. Droplets of this emulsified water tend to wet the paper and prevent the ink from taking on it uniformly.

REMEDY: Cut down the dampening moisture. If plate then tends to scum, chances are that it was not desensitized properly. (See Section 4, pages 43–44.)

Cause D: Image on deep-etched plate etched too deep. Form rollers fail to deposit ink uniformly on dots.

REMEDY: None. Have plate remade with shorter deep-etching time.

10. Non-Image Areas of Zinc Plates Discolor
or Become Slick

Cause A: Combination of too much paste drier in the ink and too much acid in the fountain water.

REMEDY: Cut down both the drier and fountain acid.

Cause B: Use of a letterpress paste drier that contains lead acetate.

REMEDY: Discard the ink. Mix fresh ink using a litho paste drier.

Cause C: An insoluble deposit of gum arabic in the plate grain, possibly due to stringy or ropy gum in the fountain water.

REMEDY: Go over the plate with a 50-50 mixture of deep-etch developer and water. When grain is clean, wash plate thoroughly with water and re-etch it.

Section 6

Offset Blanket Troubles

The most commonly used offset blankets consist of three plies of long fiber cotton fabric calendered together with a special rubber cement and then coated with a rubber compound on one side. The thickness of this rubber skim-coat varies on different makes from about 0.012 to 0.020 inch, but the over-all thickness is about 1/16 inch or 0.0625 inch. The exact thickness is not important, but individual blankets should be uniform in thickness. Accepted tolerance is ± 0.001 inch. Offset blankets are also made 2-ply, 4-ply and 5-ply for special purposes.

Accepted practice on American sheet-fed presses is to use one thickness of 3-ply blanket plus enough packing sheets to raise its surface to the proper level in relation to the cylinder bearers. This level is determined both by the press manufacturer's specifications and the image length requirement. In fact, there has to be considerable leeway from the specification in order to maintain register when paper stretches between printings in multicolor work.

Some European sheet-fed presses use two layers of offset blanket. This gives a greater "cushion" effect in the impression.

An offset blanket is wrapped around its cylinder and held under sufficient tension to prevent it from slipping on the cylinder under the rolling pressure of the printing impression. This tension can vary considerably since it is applied manually, but the average is estimated to be about 50 pounds per inch of width. When a new blanket is first installed, this tension plus the rolling-out effect of the impression may cause some stretching and make it necessary to tighten the blanket at intervals to take up the slack.

Another effect of the combined tension and rolling impression is to reduce the thickness of a new blanket during the first few thousand impressions. If the blanket thickness is measured with a micrometer and the calculated thickness of packing is added to

60

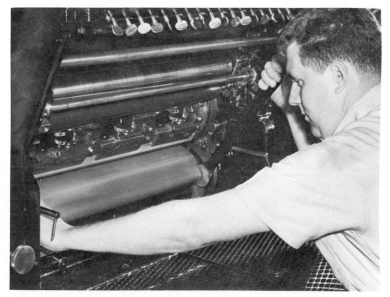

Figure 46. Tightening the Offset Blanket

Figure 47. Checking the Blanket Height with the Packing Gage

give .004 inch of impression, it may be found that, after a few hundred sheets the impression is no longer good. Checking with a packing gage may then show that the blanket has subsided .002 inch or more and needs additional packing to receive a good impression from the plate.

The skim-coat, or printing surface of blankets, was originally made from natural rubber. Nowadays, however, it is principally synthetic rubber since this has been found much less oil-absorbent and therefore much less susceptible to swelling, embossing, and the development of tackiness and glaze. In fact, tackiness of blankets has almost ceased to be a problem.

Glazing occurs, however, as a result of the absorption of some drying oils and metallic driers during printing. These promote surface oxidation which hardens the rubber and reduces its elasticity and ink receptivity. A glazed blanket fails to transfer ink properly. Removal of the glaze by scrubbing with pumice powder and solvent restores its printing quality. When in good condition the blanket surface should have a soft, velvety feel, whereas rubbing a glazed blanket with the finger produces a "chattery" sensation.

Recently a new type of offset blanket has been introduced. It consists of two layers—a base or carcass layer that is stretched around the cylinder, and a replaceable surface layer held to the base layer by means of a pressure adhesive. Since this development is still in the experimental stage, it is too early to discuss problems arising from its use.

The following are the principal troubles encountered in the use of conventional offset blankets:

1. Printed Impression Gradually Loses Sharpness or Solidity

Cause A: Loss of impression due to the blanket subsiding or becoming thinner under the rolling pressure. This trouble generally occurs with a new blanket.

REMEDY: Use the packing gage to check the height of the blanket. If it has decreased, add a packing tissue of the required thickness. If it has not changed, the trouble may be due to deterioration of the plate (see Section 5, page 56).

Cause B: Increased impression due to the blanket becoming embossed or swollen. This may be due to:
1. A blanket with insufficient solvent or oil resistance.
2. Continued use of a blanket wash that evaporates too slowly.

REMEDY: Check the height of the blanket surface with the packing gage. If it has increased, remove the indicated thickness of packing. If this does not correct the impression, check the plate image for wear and loss of ink affinity (see Section 5, page 56).

Cause C: Use of heat-set or quick-set inks with blankets designed for conventional inks. This can cause embossing and excessive pressure in the image areas.

REMEDY: Change to a blanket especially designed for heat-set and quick-set inks.

Cause D: The blanket surface has lost its ink receptiveness due to its becoming glazed and hard. Such glazing can result from oxidation of absorbed drying oils and driers, or accumulations of gum arabic.

REMEDY: Wash the blanket with solvent and water. Then scrub it with pumice powder and solvent until the glaze is removed.

2. The Image from a Previous Job Appears as a Ghost Image in Solids

Cause: The blanket is embossed as a result of ink-vehicle absorption during printing of the previous job.

REMEDY: Install a new blanket.

Note: Clean the old blanket thoroughly with blanket wash and hang it in a dark area to rest it. This will allow absorbed oil to diffuse through the rubber and may reduce the embossing.

3. Paper Tends to Stick to or be Picked by the Non-printing Areas of the Blanket

Cause: Blanket has become tacky as a result of oxidation of absorbed drying oils and the rubber. This is stimulated by manganese and/or cobalt driers. It is uncommon with modern synthetic rubber blankets.

REMEDY: Treating the blanket with a blanket lacquer or hardener will relieve the tackiness, but this relief is only temporary. The blanket should be removed, washed thoroughly, and rested until its tackiness has disappeared. It should then be scrubbed with pumice powder and solvent until its surface glaze is removed.

Note: Never use sulfur or carbon disulfide on a blanket when printing from copperized aluminum or bimetal plates. Sulfur and sulfides will blind the copper image areas.

4. The Impression is Uneven and Excessive Pressure is Required to Make All Areas Print

Cause: The blanket is not uniform in thickness. To check this, follow the procedure given in Section 2, page 26.

REMEDY: Patch up the back of the blanket in the low areas with tissues torn to the required shape, using gum arabic.

This can also be caused by one or more warped cylinders or by non-uniform tension on the blanket (see Section 3, Pages 26-27).

5. The Blanket Surface is Cut, Smashed or Indented

Cause: Accidental passage through the press of nails, wood chips, wads of paper or folded sheets, especially heavy-weight papers and paperboard.

REMEDY 1: If the surface of the blanket is cut, it can often be mended temporarily. Blanket patching compounds are available for this purpose.

REMEDY 2: If the surface of the blanket is not cut, but is smashed or indented, wash the low area thoroughly with blanket wash to swell it as much as possible. Then put paper patches under the depressed areas to bring them up to normal height. A still better method is to wash the blanket with solvent, soak the fabric backing thoroughly with water, and hang it in a dark place to rest it.

6. Horizontal Streaks in the Printing

Cause: A loose and slipping blanket. (See Section 3, page 35.)

REMEDY: Take up the slack in the blanket. Use the packing gage to check the plate-to-blanket pressure, and, if too high, remove the excess packing.

Section 7

Paper Troubles

Papers and paperboards used by lithographers come in a wide variety of types and finishes. But they all have one thing in common—they are mainly composed of cellulose fiber. They have certain properties in common such as grain direction, two-sidedness, and hygroscopic properties. But they can vary tremendously depending on the type of fiber used, the fiber preparation and the surface and finish given them in manufacture.

For satisfactory performance in lithography, sheet papers should meet the following basic requirements:

1. **Flatness**—The sheets should be flat enough to pass through the squeeze impression without wrinkling or appreciable distortion.

2. **Proper relative humidity**—To remain flat when skids or feeder piles are exposed to the pressroom atmosphere, the paper

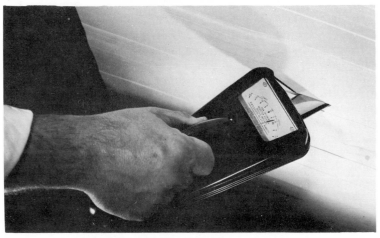

Figure 48.   Using the Paper Hygroscope to Test the
Moisture Balance of Paper

65

should have a relative humidity close to that in the pressroom. "Close" means between 8 percent RH drier and 8 percent RH more moist than the pressroom atmosphere for a single printing, and between about 4 percent RH drier and 8 percent RH more moist than the pressroom atmosphere when the job calls for two or more printings. Greater differences than these will result in wavy or tight edges that can cause distortion and misregister.

3. **Freedom from lint and dust**—Loose fibers and dust particles quickly destroy print quality.

4. **Adequate moisture resistance**—The press moisture should not soften surface sizing or coating adhesive enough to permit transfer of surface fibers, mineral filler, or coating pigment to the offset blanket.

5. **Adequate pick resistance**—Surface strength should be sufficient to prevent picking without excessive reduction of ink tack.

6. **Freedom from active chemicals**—Paper should contain no chemical that tends to sensitize printing plates and cause scumming, or to emulsify the ink and cause tinting.

7. **Good ink-drying qualities.**

8. **Accurate trimming**—Sheets should be trimmed with edges straight and corners square. A convex or concave gripper edge can cause register trouble especially in printing thin, flexible papers.

In addition to these basic requirements, there are certain qualities that are desirable or are required for special types of work.

In general, sheet papers for multicolor work should be grain-long. Dimensional changes, which are much greater across than with the grain, can then be compensated for by changes in plate and blanket packing to maintain register. There are exceptional cases, however, where grain-short paper is desirable, namely, where sheet to sheet misregister, embossing of solids, tail-end curl, or folding and binding requirements are problems. However, grain-short paper should never be used when more than one printing is required since its dimensional changes across the press cannot be compensated for.

Dimensional stability or resistance to mechanical stretch is important in multicolor work, whether done in one or several printings. The rolling impression, together with the gripper pull required to separate sheets from the blanket, stretches them. If the paper is sufficiently stretch resistant, this stretch is purely elastic and the sheets return to their original size. But if there is any permanent stretch, it will vary from sheet to sheet and make register of subsequent colors impossible. Embossed and pebbled papers are most likely to give trouble of this type.

After being printed, some thin papers have a tendency to curl toward the printed side. This is caused by the slight moistening they get through contact with the offset blanket. Such curl can render labels, wrappers and other printed articles unusable. Paper can be tested for curling tendency and rejected if it is excessive.

For a detailed discussion of paper and paperboard, offset paper troubles, and tests for printability and print quality, see LTF Publication No. 308, "What the Lithographer Should Know About Paper."

The following is a list of the principal paper troubles encountered by pressmen, with their causes and remedies:

1. The Paper Wrinkles or Creases

Cause A: Front guides, insertion device or cylinder grippers are not functioning properly.

REMEDY: This is a press problem. (See Section 1, page 20.)

Cause B: If the wrinkle starts near the center of the sheets and extends clear to their back edges, the paper is wavy-edged.

Figure 49.   End of Paper Skid Showing Wavy Edges

Courtesy of Southworth Machine Co.

Figure 50.   Cabinet-type Paper Conditioner

REMEDY 1: Recondition the paper in a paper-conditioning machine to remove excess moisture from edges or to add moisture to body of sheets.

REMEDY 2: Apply heat to the sides of the feeder pile to warm the edges of the sheets and drive out some of their moisture. This can be done by placing strip heaters or infra-red lamps along the sides of the feeder pile near the top. Or the load can be placed in a hot, dry area for an hour or more before printing. This remedy is not recommended for register trouble.

REMEDY 3: If the press has multiple front guides, adjust the end guides to let the front corners of the sheet go forward slightly.

REMEDY 4: If the press has a three-point guide system, use a bustle to put a slight kink or wave in the gripper edge of the sheets. This pulls the front corners together slightly relieving the lateral compression on the back half of the sheets.

REMEDY 5: Cut out sections of packing under the side edges of the blanket where there is no printing. This relieves pressure on the wavy edges of the sheets that causes "fanning in."

Cause C: If the wrinkle starts between the gripper edge and center of the sheets and disappears before reaching their back edges, the paper is tight-edged or baggy.

REMEDY 1: Recondition the paper in a paper-conditioning machine to add moisture to the edges or to remove excess moisture from the body of the sheets.

REMEDY 2: Cut out sections of packing under the side edges of the blanket where there is no printing. This relieves the pressure on the tight edges that causes "fanning out."

2. Misregister—Two or More Printings

Colors fit along gripper edge, but fail to fit at the back corners.

Cause A: If second printing is longer across the back edge than the first printing, the side edges of the sheets have picked up moisture between printings and become either less tight-edged or more wavy-edged than they were originally.

REMEDY 1: The best remedy is prevention. Sheets should be flat for the first printing, and should print same length as plate image along their back edge. This can easily be determined with the LTF Register Rule. Between printings, the piles should be covered with moisture-vapor-proof covers to prevent pick-up or loss of moisture.

REMEDY 2: See remedies for back edge wrinkles caused by wavy-edged paper (1-B, above).

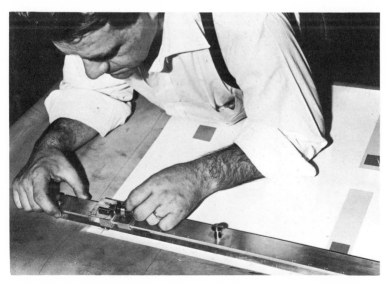

Cause B: If second printing is shorter than the first printing across the back edge, the side edges of the sheets have lost moisture between printings and become either less wavy-edged or more tight-edged than they were originally.

REMEDY 1: Here again, the best remedy is prevention (see Cause A, Remedy 1, above).

REMEDY 2: See cause and remedies for center wrinkles caused by tight edges (1-C above).

3. Misregister—Two or More Printings

Colors fail to fit lengthwise along the gripper edge.

Cause A: If second printing falls inside the first printing on the off-guide side, the sheets have expanded crosswise between printings due to moisture pick-up in the first printing. This should not happen with grain long paper but almost always happens if the paper is grain short.

REMEDY 1: Recondition the paper to remove excess moisture.

REMEDY 2: Remake the plate. Use the first printing as a key and step the subjects out to fit it.

REMEDY 3: Split the plate and spread the halves to get an approximate fit.

Cause B: If second printing is same width as first printing, but side register varies from sheet to sheet, the side guide is not functioning properly.

REMEDY: This is a press problem. (See Section 1, page 18.)

Cause C: If second printing is same length from front to back as the first printing but register varies from sheet to sheet, the front guides, sheet-forwarding mechanism or grippers are not functioning properly. Another possible cause is backlash in the cylinder drive gears which prevents exact synchronization of plate and blanket cylinders.

REMEDY: These are press problems. (See Section 1, pages 15 and 16.)

4. Misregister—Two or More Printings

The second printing is consistently longer or shorter from front to back than the first printing.

Cause: The plate and blanket are not properly packed to give the desired print length.

REMEDY 1: If the second printing is longer than the first, the blanket is packed too high. Transfer packing sheets from the blanket to the plate cylinder until the print is shortened sufficiently to register.

REMEDY 2: If the second printing is shorter than the first, the plate is packed too high. Transfer packing sheets from the plate to the blanket cylinder until the print is lengthened sufficiently to register.

Note 1: The change in image length caused by transfer of a packing sheet can be calculated approximately by the following formula:

$\Delta L = p \times .0125 \times X$

where $\Delta L =$ Change in image length.

      $p =$ Thickness of packing sheet in mils (.001″).

      $X =$ Fraction of cylinder circumference occupied by plate image.

Example:

        $p = .001″$

        $X = .66$

Then $\Delta L = .001 \times .0125 \times .66$

            $= .008$ inch increase or decrease in length.

Note 2: When a job requires multiple printings, it is always good practice to run the first color short—in other words, with the plate packed somewhat above bearer height. This allows more leeway to lengthen the succeeding impressions to compensate for paper stretch due to moisture pick-up and the ironing-out effect of the squeeze impression.

5. Misregister—Two or More Printings

The second printing registers at the gripper edge but shows variable sheet to sheet misregister along the back edge that cannot be corrected by adjustments in the plate and blanket packing.

Cause A: Some sheets have stretched more than others from front to back in one or both of the printings. This sometimes happens with lightweight papers that have been multiple-roll-sheeted at the mill. The sheets from some rolls stretch more than others.

REMEDY: The best remedy is prevention. Any such variable mechanical stretch should be caught at the start of the first printing. Register marks, front and back, bleeding to the side edges of the sheet will show such variable stretch in delivered sheets.

The trouble may be caused by paper lacking in stretch resistance across its grain. It could also be caused by excessive back-cylinder pressure. If reducing the pressure to that normally required to give a good print does not eliminate the variable stretch that causes sheet to sheet misregister, the paper should be discarded as unsuitable for multicolor printing.

Cause B: Cockled or embossed papers. These papers are not truly flat. When printed, the squeeze impression rolls them flat momentarily producing dimensional changes and distortion that varies from sheet to sheet. Their original dimensions may be wholly or only partly recovered after printing. Embossing also weakens paper, making it more susceptible to permanent mechanical stretch.

REMEDY: Misregister can be minimized only by printing with as little pressure as possible. But a pressure that will permit good register is often not enough to produce a good impression. For this reason, it is not advisable to attempt close register work on cockled or embossed papers, especially in large sheets.

Cause C: Large solids on some areas of the sheets. The high gripper tension required to separate such solid areas from the offset blanket stretches the sheets permanently in these areas while the other areas remain unstretched. Sometimes the stretched solid areas appear to be embossed. Often this stretch varies from sheet to sheet making it impossible to fit succeeding colors.

REMEDY: Reduce the tack of the ink as much as is possible without affecting print quality. If this does not help, change to a stronger or heavier paper.

6. Misregister—Single Printing on a Multicolor Press

Colors fit along the gripper edge, but fail to fit at the back corners. This trouble occurs less frequently than when two or more printings are involved. The interval between impressions on a multicolor press is normally about one second—too short a time for the sheets to lose their original flatness or to change in degree of waviness or tight edge.

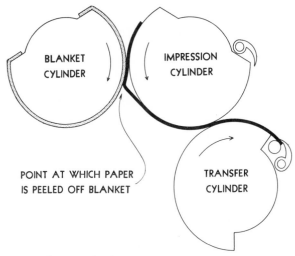

Figure 52. Diagram Showing How Paper Adheres to the Blanket in
Solid Areas Causing Stretch, Embossing and Curl

Cause A: If the colors are printing longer across the back edge of
the sheets than the plate image, the paper is wavy-edged. This can
easily be determined with the LTF Register Rule. It would not
cause misregister if each sheet distorted in exactly the same way in
the successive printing units. Unfortunately the distortion generally
varies slightly from unit to unit resulting in back edge misregister
which varies from sheet to sheet.

REMEDY 1: The best remedy is to prevent sheet distortion—
in other words, to use reasonably flat paper. The worse the distortion, the worse the misregister will be.

REMEDY 2: See remedies for back edge wrinkles caused by
wavy-edged paper (1-B, page 67).

Cause B: If the colors are printing shorter across the back edge of
the sheets than the plate image, the paper is tight-edged. This is
easily determined with the LTF Register Rule. Normally, tight-
edged paper causes less trouble than wavy-edged paper. But if the
tight-edge condition is bad enough, it can cause misregister in the
body of the sheets, and even wrinkling or creasing.

REMEDY 1: The best remedy is reasonably flat paper to start
with. The worse the distortion, the worse the misregister will be.

REMEDY 2: See remedies for center wrinkles caused by tight-
edged paper (1-C, page 68).

7. Slur in Halftones and at the Back
Edge of Solids

This can be caused by too much back-cylinder pressure in printing coated stock, too much plate-to-blanket pressure when running smooth, ungrained plates, or running too much ink. It can also be caused by the rippling of sheets as they enter the impression causing some areas to contact the blanket prematurely. Slur is discussed in Section 2, page 28.

8. Doubling of Halftones on Multicolor Presses

Doubling is a form of misregister in which the ink printed by one unit prints back from the blanket of the following unit out of register with the print-back from the preceding sheet. Its causes and remedies are described in Section 2, pages 31 and 32. One cause is sheet distortion due to wavy-or tight-edged paper.

9. Solids Are Marred by Many White, Fiber-shaped
Spots, and Halftones are Grainy

Cause A: Uncoated paper with loosely bonded surface fibers variously referred to as lint, fuzz, fluff and whiskers. These fibers are lifted by tacky inks even when printing a single color. Once attached to the blanket or plate, they absorb moisture and refuse to transfer ink.

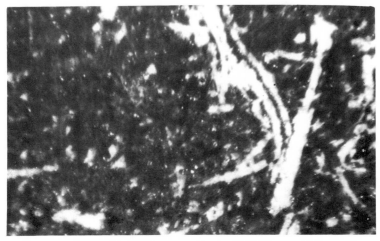

Figure 53.   Blow-up of Solid Printed on Linty Paper

REMEDY 1: Reduce the tack of the ink as much as possible without affecting print quality. If the paper still lints, it should be discarded or press sized.

REMEDY 2: Print a transparent size such as Laketine or alumina hydrate ink on the paper using a blank plate and no dampening. Allow the size to dry before printing the job.

Cause B: Surface-sized paper in which the surface fibers are not well bonded by hydration but to a large extent are held down by the starch surface size. Such papers usually cause no trouble on a single-color press. But, on a multicolor press, moisture from the first unit softens the surface size so that fibers are lifted by the second-down or a later ink.

REMEDY 1: Reduce the plate dampening to a minimum. If necessary, try adding a little wetting agent to the dampening water to help reduce the amount needed.

REMEDY 2: Try adding one part of isopropyl alcohol to three parts of dampening solution. This may reduce its softening effect on the starch surface size.

REMEDY 3: Press size the paper prior to printing (see A-2, above).

Cause C: Cotton fibers coming from molleton or other fabric dampening roller covers. These are generally easy to distinguish from paper fibers. Usually they are fewer in number and their average length is more than one-eighth inch. Paper fibers are usually shorter.

REMEDY 1: Put new covers on the dampeners.

REMEDY 2: Change to parchment paper dampener covers or one of the newer plate dampening systems. (See Section 4)

10. Solids Printed on Uncoated Paper Look and Feel Rough

Cause: The surface fibers are not well bonded and are raised, but not actually picked up, by the pull of the ink. This can happen in printing a single color. It can also happen on the second or a later unit in multicolor presswork.

REMEDIES: The same remedies apply as in the case of linty paper (see No. 7, above).

11. Prints are Marred by Non-fiber-shaped White Spots

The spots repeat on consecutive sheets and increase in number during the run.

Cause A: Loose paper dust on the sheets. This can be slitter dust, cutter dust, or drier scale.

REMEDY 1: Install a vacuum sheet cleaner. (Such cleaners are reported to remove much dust, but are not 100 percent effective.)

REMEDY 2: Give the paper a dry run through a press before printing the job. This will lift or shake off most of the dust particles.

Cause B: Flakes of coating or particles larger than single fibers picked from the paper surface. To distinguish them from loose dust particles, thumb down through the printed sheets to the sheet on which a typical spot first appeared. If examination with a magnifier shows that the paper surface in the original spot was ruptured, the paper was picked. If not, the spot was caused by a loose dust particle.

REMEDY: Reduce the ink's tack as much as possible without affecting print quality. If this does not help, the paper is unsuitable for offset.

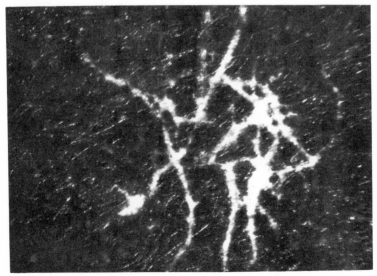

Figure 54.   Blow-up of Typical Spot Caused by Paper Dust

12. Paper Picks, Splits or Blisters

Picking refers to rupturing of the paper surface in areas larger than single fibers by the pull of the ink.

In **splitting**, large areas of the paper are peeled off and stick to the blanket. These often develop into V-shaped tears extending to the back edge of the sheets.

Blistering occurs when the pull of the ink causes internal separation or delamination without actual rupture of the paper surface.

Picking, splitting and blistering almost always occur or start in solids, seldom in halftone areas. They are most likely to occur in solids near the back edge of the sheets. Therefore, whenever possible, layout of the form should be made with solid areas away from the back edge.

Cause A: The internal bond strength of the paper is too low or the bonding of coating to the base stock is too weak to withstand the pull of the ink.

REMEDY 1: Have the paper tested. If its pick resistance is normal, see Cause B. If it is weak, reduce the ink's tack with a suitable reducer or solvent. If this reduces print quality too much, change to a more pick-resistant paper.

Figure 55.   Paper Picked and Torn Near Back Edge of Sheets

REMEDY 2: If reducing the ink's tack affects print quality too much and better paper is not available, try reducing the press speed.

Cause B: The paper has good pick resistance when dry but is weakened by successive applications of moisture in multicolor presswork. In this case, the first-down color prints OK, but the second, third or fourth color picks the paper.

REMEDY 1: Reduce both the plate moisture and the back-cylinder pressure to a minimum. If this does not help, change to a better paper.

REMEDY 2: If no better paper is available, press size the paper with a transparent white ink using a blank plate and no moisture. Allow the size to dry before printing.

(For other causes of picking, see Section 8, page 88. See also LTF Publications No. 308, page 67, and No. 310, page 148.)

13. Paper Slips In, or Pulls Out of the Grippers

This is a press or ink trouble and is not the fault of the paper. (See Section 1, page 20, and Section 2, page 32.)

14. Sheets Curl on Delivery and Fail to Jog Properly

This occurs principally in printing lightweight papers.

Cause A: Press moisture is expanding the printed side of the paper, causing the sheets to curl downward. In extreme cases, the sheets roll up like mailing tubes. (See Figure 25, page 21.)

REMEDY 1: Reduce the press moisture to a minimum. If the trouble persists, try adding a little wetting agent to the dampening water to help reduce the amount needed.

REMEDY 2: Try adding one part of isopropyl alcohol to three parts of dampening solution. This may reduce its tendency to swell the paper fibers. It may also reduce the amount of dampening needed. If the above remedies do not stop the curl, the paper is unsuitable for lithography.

Cause B: Printed sheets have a back edge curl (tail-end hook) so that the rear jogger is ineffective. This results when heavy solids are printed near their back edge.

REMEDY 1: Reduce the ink's tack as much as possible without sacrificing print quality.

REMEDY 2: Reduce the back-cylinder pressure to a minimum.

REMEDY 3: Try to avoid layouts having solids near the back edge.

15. Sheets Curl Toward Their Printed Side after Standing for a Time in Delivery Piles

This occurs mostly with thin papers that tend to curl downward on delivery (see 14-A above). The original curl reverses after the sheets stand in the pile.

Cause A: Press moisture swells the paper's surface fibers and relaxes them. Then, when dry, they shrink to a new formation without their original tensions. This new formation results in shrinkage of the entire surface and curl toward the printed side. (See LTF Publication, No. 308, page 28)

REMEDY 1: Keep dampening to a minimum. If the plate requires excessive moisture, get a new, better desensitized plate.

REMEDY 2: If job is completed and the curl discovered before the sheets are cut, run the sheets through a single-color press, using a blank plate and dampening to apply moisture to the back side of the sheets.

Cause B: Paper with excessive curling tendency.
REMEDY: Avoid such paper. Paper can be pre-tested for curling tendency. (See LTF Publication No. 308, pages 125–128)

Figure 56.   Pack of Labels Showing Permanent Curl Due to Press Moisture

Figure 57. Skid of Printed Labels Showing Embossed Solid Areas

16. Paper "Embosses" in Solid Areas

Solid areas in the printed sheets are slightly curled and protrude upward giving an embossed effect. This trouble is most prevalent with lightweight papers such as label stocks.

Cause: Simultaneous stretching due to weakness of the stock, and sharp angle peel-off from the blanket caused by tack of the ink.

REMEDY 1: Reduce the ink's tack as much as possible without sacrificing print quality.

REMEDY 2: If the work is done on a multicolor press in a single printing, run the paper grain short. In this case, care must be taken that the paper is reasonably flat. Otherwise distortion and misregister will result. If register requirements are very critical, avoid this remedy.

17. Paper Coating Piles or Builds on the Blanket's Non-printing Areas

A little such piling does not usually affect print quality. But it can continue to accumulate until halftones become sandy and highlight dots are lost.

Cause: Running coated or film-coated paper in which the coating adhesive is water-soluble (lacks wet-rub resistance).

Figure 58.   Offset Blanket Showing Coating Pile in Non-Printing Areas

REMEDY 1: Avoid coated papers that have poor wet-rub resistance. (See LTF Publication No. 308, page 142.)

REMEDY 2: Try adding one part of isopropyl alcohol to three parts of dampening solution. This reduces the solubility of starch coating adhesives. It works best with Dahlgren dampening systems. (See Section 4, page 41).

18. Paper Coating Piles in the Middle Halftone Printing Areas of the Blanket

After one to two thousand impressions, the middle halftones develop a mottled appearance due to dot slur, and the blanket shows a lumpy build-up in those areas. This happens only on the second or later unit of multicolor presses—never on the first unit.

Cause: The coating adhesive is being softened and rendered tacky by moisture on the first unit so that ink on the following unit can lift traces of adhesive and coating pigment. These mix with the ink producing a combination that sticks to the blanket and gradually

Figure 59a. Blow-up of 2-Color Halftone at Start of Run
—Black Second-down

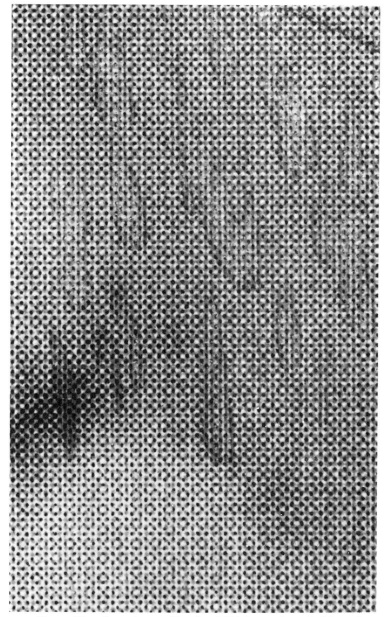

Figure 59b.   Same Area as 59a after 2,000 Impressions: Build-up of
Paper Coating on Black Blanket Caused Slurred Pattern

produces a pile of appreciable thickness. Frequent blanket wash-ups with water and ink solvent are needed to remove it. Strangely enough, papers that cause this trouble generally show good wet-rub resistance.

REMEDY 1: The best remedy is to change to a better paper. Unfortunately, there is no reliable test for papers that cause this trouble. (See LTF Publication, No. 308, page 144)

REMEDY 2: Try adding one part of isopropyl alcohol to each three parts of the dampening solution on all but the last press unit.

REMEDY 3: Press size the paper with a transparent white ink using a blank plate and no moisture. Allow the size to dry before printing.

19. An Over-All Tint Quickly Appears on the Unprinted Areas of Coated Paper

This tint may appear on the non-image areas of the plates but can be washed off with the water sponge. If another paper is sub-stituted, the tint disappears, but quickly returns on going back to the original paper.

Cause: The fountain solution is extracting an ink-emulsifying agent from the paper coating.

REMEDY: Stiffen the ink as much as possible with No. 8 varnish or body gum or try another stiffer ink. Avoid the use of any wet-ting agent in the fountain water. If tinting continues, get another paper.

Note: Tinting can also be caused by a press plate con-dition (Section 5, page 55), or by unsatisfactory ink (Section 8, page 90).

Section 8

Ink Troubles

Basically, lithographic ink is a dispersion of pigment in a fluid vehicle. The pigment provides the color and determines whether the printed ink film will be transparent or will have covering power. The vehicle gives the ink fluidity so that it can be distributed by the press inking rollers and applied evenly to the form. And, in the printed ink film, the vehicle must change or be changed to a solid in order to bind the pigment to the printed surface.

Although basically the same, inks supplied to lithographers vary widely in formulation and properties. This is because of the wide range of surfaces being printed, the characteristics of different presses, and the various end-use requirements of printed jobs. There are inks for general commercial work that can be adjusted by the lithographer to fit a wide variety of papers. There are also inks designed especially for label printing, posters, magazine covers, greeting cards, decalcomamias, foils, plastics, metal decorating and other purposes. These are usually press-ready, and require little or no adjustment by the lithographer. And, regardless of the surface to be printed, inks can be varied as to transparency, finish, rub- and scuff-resistance, fastness to light, and resistance to heat, chemicals and solvents, to meet the various end-use requirements.

Inks can also be varied as to their method of drying. Conventional inks contain principally drying oils, and dry by a combination of absorption and chemical action, namely, oxidation and polymerization. Quick-set inks contain drying oils and resins, plus solvents that speed up their setting by a process of selective absorption. Their final drying is also by oxidation and polymerization. They are best united to printing on coated papers and boards.

The vehicle in heat-set inks is principally resin dissolved in a solvent. These inks are designed for web presswork where the printed web can be passed through an oven or over a hot cylinder to drive off the solvent, leaving only the resin to bind the pigment.

Even so, some drying oil and driers are usually added to increase rub- and scuff-resistance. Heat-set inks are seldom used on sheet-fed presses.

The basic requirement for all lithographic inks that distinguishes them from letterpress inks is that they must work with moisture. Dampening water always mixes to some extent with the ink during printing, but the ink must not waterlog and become pasty. Neither may it break down and mix with the water; otherwise a tint of the ink would be printed over the entire sheet. The ink maker selects the proper pigments and vehicles and adjusts the ink's body to meet these requirements.

In view of the foregoing, it can readily be seen that the variables in ink making and lithography are almost infinite. Therefore in the use of ink, the offset pressman is constantly faced with problems that require knowledge, experience and good judgment to solve. Knowledge can be gained through study and for this purpose LTF has issued its Publication No. 310, "What the Lithographer Should Know About Ink." Experience and judgment come with practice. The ink maker, of course, should not be forgotten. In cases of doubt regarding the use of driers, or the best materials with which to adjust his inks, the ink maker is the best source of dependable advice.

It is hoped that this section will give the pressman a ready reference that will help him to avoid ink troubles or to quickly and correctly diagnose them when they arise and apply the proper remedies.

1. Ink Sets Off in the Delivery Pile

Cause A: The ink is not properly adjusted to the absorbency of the surface being printed. It fails to set before the following sheet contacts it on the delivery pile. This can be due to the ink vehicle penetrating the paper too slowly, or to paper that lacks absorbency.

REMEDY 1: Add one half to one ounce of boiled linseed oil or #0000 varnish per pound of ink. An even smaller amount of heat-set or quick-set solvent will accomplish the same result.

REMEDY 2: If the trouble occurs in printing on coated paper with conventional ink, change to a quick-set ink.

REMEDY 3: Add a small amount of anti-offset compound to speed up setting of the ink by shortening it. Use as little as possible since an excess will reduce the ink's rub- and scuff-resistance, and prevent trapping and adhesion of inks in succeeding printings.

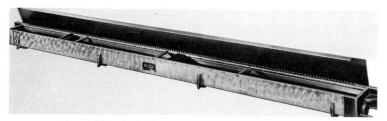

Figure 60.   Anti-offset Dry Spray Attachment for Press

REMEDY 4: Use an anti-offset spray, either wet or dry. Keep the amount to a minimum, especially if the job requires additional printings or good scuff-resistance.

REMEDY 5: On most large presses it is possible to install a bank of infra-red lamps so that sheets pass them as they travel toward the delivery pile. The heat speeds up setting and drying of the ink.

REMEDY 6: Avoid high piling of sheets on the delivery. In the case of aluminum foil and plastics, remove the sheets from the delivery in small lifts and rack them for drying.

Cause B: Rough handling of skids of freshly printed sheets.

REMEDY 1: Avoid lowering delivery skid to floor too fast with resultant jarring of the load.

REMEDY 2: Avoid trucking skids over rough floors. Avoid sudden starts and stops in trucking.

Cause C: Running too much ink. The more ink the more slowly setting takes place.

REMEDY: Run a stronger ink and run it spare. Reduce the water to a minimum.

Cause D: Sheets embossed or waffled in printing. When solids are embossed, succeeding sheets contact the embossed areas before the ink on them has set. The normal air cushion is not effective during jogging. (See Section 7, page 80.)

REMEDY 1: Increase the penetrating power of the ink (see A-1, above).

REMEDY 2: If possible, secure paper with less embossing tendency. If the work is done in a single printing on a multicolor press, try running the paper grain short. (See Section 7, page 80.)

Cause E: Curly or bumpy paper. Such paper acts similarly to paper embossed in printing (Cause D, above).

REMEDY: Increase the ink's penetration and setting rate. Run the ink spare.

Cause F: Printing with gloss inks. Gloss is obtained with inks having minimum penetration on paper with high ink hold-out. Waxes in gloss inks tend to prevent offsetting, but for the highest gloss they are usually ineffective.

REMEDY: Use wet or dry anti-offset spray. Use as little as possible. An excess will reduce rub- and scuff-resistance. Do not allow sheets to pile high on the delivery, but remove and let them dry in small lifts.

2. Ink Picks, Splits or Tears the Paper

This can be either an ink or a paper trouble. Either the ink is excessively tacky, or the paper has too little pick resistance for printing with an ink having normal tack for the press size and desired speed. Since picking, splitting and blistering troubles are mostly caused by paper weakness, they are also discussed in Section 7, page 77.

Cause A: The ink is too tacky for the paper.

REMEDY: Reduce the ink's tack with a suitable reducer or solvent. If this reduces print quality too much, change to a more pick-resistant paper.

Cause B: Conventional ink is drying and increasing in tack on the press. This can be due to too much cobalt drier in the ink.

REMEDY 1: Add a little #00 varnish to the ink to reduce its initial tack.

REMEDY 2: Add a little "slow-dry" or anti-oxidant compound to the ink (consult ink maker).

REMEDY 3: Mix a fresh batch of ink with less drier.

Cause C: Quick-set or heat-set ink is losing solvent and increasing in tack during press stops. This can be due to absorption of solvent by newly covered rubber ink rollers, or to evaporation, or both.

REMEDY 1: If the roller composition is new, or if the rollers have been standing dry for any length of time, saturate them with an ink solvent before inking up the press.

REMEDY 2: When starting the run, use "start-up" inks that contain no volatile solvents.

REMEDY 3: If "start-up" inks are not available, soften the press ink at the start to counteract the stiffening due to loss of solvent by evaporation during makeready. Once the run is started and the ink flow established, the regular ink should cause no trouble.

REMEDY 4: During press stops, spray the ink rollers with heat-set oil to keep the ink from drying.

Cause D: Quick-set ink continues to pick the paper after the run has started.

REMEDY: Reduce the tack of the ink or have it reformulated with a less volatile solvent.

3. Ink Backs Away from the Fountain Roller

Cause: The ink sets up in the fountain and fails to flow and replace the ink that is removed by the fountain roller.

REMEDY 1: Work the ink in the fountain frequently to keep it fluid. Better yet, install an ink fountain agitator.

REMEDY 2: With some inks, the addition of a little long varnish (#3 or #4) will increase their length and flow properties.

4. The Ink Piles or Cakes on the Rollers, Plate or Blanket and Fails to Transfer Properly

Cause A: The ink is too short and lacks the fluidity necessary to make it transfer or lift properly.

REMEDY 1: Add a varnish that will lengthen the ink. Consult the ink maker as to the proper varnish to use.

REMEDY 2: Reduce the dampening to a minimum. (Some inks can become too short as a result of waterlogging.) If this does not help, have the ink made with a more water-resistant varnish.

Cause B: The ink is poorly ground and contains too many coarse particles or aggregates. These are not transferred, but remain and build up a cake on the roller, plate and blanket surfaces.

REMEDY: Regrind the ink or return it to the ink maker to be reground (see LTF Publication #310, page 185).

Cause C: The ink contains a coarse, heavy pigment, the particles of which tend to pile.

REMEDY: Consult the ink maker. Have the ink reformulated.

Cause D: Paper coating that becomes tacky when moistened. In multicolor presswork, moisture applied by the first unit softens the coating so that some of it is picked up by the blanket on the second or a later unit. This gradually builds up on the blanket in the middle halftone areas forming "bumps" that cause slur and produce a mottled appearance. (See Section 7, page 81.)

REMEDY 1: Press size the paper with a transparent white ink.

REMEDY 2: Change to a coated paper that has better moisture resistance.

5. The Ink Breaks Down and Tints in the Unprinted Areas

The tint can be seen on the printed sheets and may or may not be visible on the plate. It is not tight to the plate but can be washed off with water. However, it quickly reappears when printing is resumed.

Cause A: The ink is not sufficiently water-resistant and emulsifies slightly in the dampening moisture.

REMEDY 1: If the ink is soft or soupy, add some #8 varnish to increase its tack and "pull it together."

REMEDY 2: If the ink is short and tends to waterlog, add some water-resistant varnish.

Cause B: The ink is too fresh. The vehicle has not had time to wet the pigment thoroughly.

REMEDY: Allow the ink to stand a week or more before using it.

Cause C: Wetting agents and/or chemicals in paper coating extracted by the fountain water are causing the ink to emulsify. This is indicated if the tinting stops when another paper is substituted.

REMEDY: Try stiffening the ink with long varnish (#8 or #10) or water-resistant varnish. If this does not help, change to another paper. (See also Section 7, page 84.)

Cause D: The press plate is slightly ink sensitive due to residues of plate coating materials remaining on its non-image areas. (For identification of this plate condition and its treatment, see Section 5, page 55.)

6. Ink Causes the Printing Plate to Scum

Scum is usually visible on the plate and cannot be removed with the water sponge. If very light, it can sometimes be removed by re-etching the plate.

Cause A: Running too much or too soft an ink on halftones. The ink squashes and spreads over the non-printing areas between the dots, gradually sensitizing them.

REMEDY: Run the ink on halftones as stiff and spare as possible.

Cause B: Abrasive particles in the ink. These gradually wear the plate at the margins of its image areas causing dots and lines to thicken.

REMEDY: Have the ink reground or replace it with a better ink.

Cause C: Too much drier or compound in the ink.

REMEDY: Use as little drier as possible. If conditions require more than one ounce of regular drier per pound, use a concentrated drier. Avoid adding compounds whenever possible.

Note: Other causes of plate sensitization and scumming are discussed in Section 3, page 34, Section 4, page 43, and Section 5, page 52.

7. Ink Dries Too Slowly or Fails to Dry— Conventional and Quick-Set Inks

Failure of ink to dry is usually not discovered until the job or part of it has been run. Saving such a job can be much more expensive than prevention of the trouble.

Cause A: Insufficient drier in the ink.

REMEDY 1: Prevent this trouble by making a drying test of the ink on the paper to be printed before starting the job. (See LTF Publication No. 310, page 187.)

Figure 61. NPIRI Drying Time Recorder

REMEDY 2: Overprint the wet ink with a transparent size containing drier, or with overprint varnish.

REMEDY 3: Run the wet sheets through a single-color offset press without ink, water, or pressure, using wet-spray equipment to spray a solution of drier onto the sheets. A suitable solution is one part of cobalt octoate in ten parts of naptha having a flash point not less than 100° F.

Cause B: The moisture content of the paper is too high. Excess moisture can be in paper when received, or can result from running too much dampening solution.

REMEDY 1: Test the paper with a sword hygrometer. If its RH is found to be above 60 percent, add more than the normal amount of drier or, preferably, a stronger drier. Make a drying test on the stock to be printed before going to press.

REMEDY 2: Wind the printed sheets to let excess moisture out, or hang the sheets in a paper-conditioning machine with air circulation.

REMEDY 3: See Remedies 2 and 3 under Cause A, above.

Cause C: The paper has a low pH value (below about 4.5 for uncoated or 6.0 for coated paper).

REMEDY 1: Make a drying test on the paper to be printed before starting to print. Add more or a stronger drier if necessary.

REMEDY 2: See Remedies 2 and 3 under Cause A, above.

Cause D: Too much acid in the dampening water.

REMEDY 1: Avoid this trouble by keeping the fountain solution pH above 4.5 and preferably between 5.0 and 6.0.

REMEDY 2: To save the job, see Remedies 2 and 3 under Cause A, above.

Cause E: Lack of available oxygen to dry the ink. This can happen in printing large areas of heavy solids.

REMEDY: Wind the sheets several times during the drying period.

Cause F: Temperature of the pressroom or of the paper is too low.

REMEDY 1: Avoid this trouble by maintaining the pressroom temperature at 75° to 80° F constantly. If this is not practical, one of the following expedients should help:

1. Install infra-red lamps over the feed board to warm the paper as it is fed.
2. Install infra-red lamps over the delivery pile to warm the sheets as they are delivered.
3. Install gas flames to contact the sheets as they pass from the last printing unit to the delivery.

In any case provision should be made to shut off the heat the moment printing is interrupted.

REMEDY 2: Allow cold paper to reach pressroom temperature before starting to print. Keep it wrapped to avoid the development of wavy edges.

8. Ink Chalks on Coated Paper

Chalking is the condition where the ink appears dry but can easily be rubbed off leaving the stock bare.

Cause A: Excessive vehicle penetration. Either paper with high absorbency, or a strongly penetrating ink vehicle can be the cause.

REMEDY: Add body gum (#8 or #10 varnish), gelled varnish, gloss varnish, or a binding varnish to decrease the vehicle's penetration rate.

Figure 62.   Chalking Due to Slow
Drying of Ink on Coated Paper

Cause B: Delayed drying. If drying is too slow, too much vehicle is absorbed before gelling takes place and the pigment is left without sufficient binder.

REMEDY 1: Review the causes of delayed drying of conventional and quick-set inks. (See No. 7, page 91.) Any one of these could be the cause of chalking. Apply the indicated remedy.

REMEDY 2: Chalking is not evident until hours after the sheets are printed. However, a chalked job can usually be saved by overprinting the work with a transparent size or overprint varnish to supply the required binder.

9. An Ink is Dry but Rubs Off in Folding and Binding Operations

Cause: Weak film formation caused by non-drying materials in the ink.

REMEDY: Keep additions of anti-offset compound, wax compound, cup grease, petrolatum, or mineral oil to a minimum. All non-drying materials plasticize the dried ink film and decrease its rub-resistance. Driers usually contain some non-drying components, so excessive drier should be avoided.

Figure 63.   Smudging Due to Lack of Rub-Resistance of Dried Ink Film

10. Dried Ink on Labels, Box Wraps or Cartons is Scuffed or Marred in Use

Cause A: The ink is not scuff-proof on the printed stock.

REMEDY: Obtain inks made to be scuff-proof on the particular stock to be printed. Ink that is scuff-proof on one stock is not necessarily scuff-proof on another. Making and testing proofs before printing the job will enable selection of suitable inks (see LTF Publication No. 310, "What the Lithographer Should Know About Ink," page 194).

Figure 64.   Sutherland Rub Tester: Used to Check Rub- and Scuff-proofness

11. Ink Fails to Trap on a Previously Printed and Dried Color

In pressroom language, the previously printed ink has crystallized. Actually, a non-drying oil or wax has oozed to its surface, making it non-receptive to fresh ink.

Cause A: Too much grease or wax compound in the dried ink.

REMEDY 1: Avoid grease and wax compounds in inks where a second printing is to follow. Keep drier to a minimum since driers usually contain some non-drying materials.

REMEDY 2: Make succeeding printings as soon as the previous ink is dry enough to permit handling the sheets. The longer an ink is allowed to dry, the more non-drying materials will ooze to its surface and interfere with trapping.

REMEDY 3: Where driers are added to ink by the pressman, it is safer to use paste drier in the first-down colors. If cobalt drier is used, it should be kept to a minimum.

REMEDY 4: Add a trapping compound to the ink that fails to trap. Ink makers can supply this.

Figure 65. Blow-up Showing Ink that Trapped on Dried Under-color, but lacked Adhesion and Rubbed off Easily after Drying

12. An Ink Traps on a Previously Printed and Dried Color but, When Dry, it Lacks Adhesion

Cause A: The first-down ink has crystallized—not enough to prevent trapping, but enough to prevent adhesion.

Cause B: A trapping compound has enabled the second-down ink to trap on a crystallized color, but without good adhesion. In both cases, the second-down ink, after drying can easily be scratched off with the fingernail.

REMEDY 1: Prevent crystallization of the first-down ink (see No. 11, page 96).

REMEDY 2: Run the printed sheets through the drying oven of a spirit varnishing machine. Heating improves the adhesion and may save the job.

13. Ink Fails to Trap in Wet Multicolor Printing

Cause A: Too much tack in relation to the preceding ink. This is particularly true in metal decorating and in printing on aluminum foil and non-absorbent stocks like decalcomania papers. The more absorbent the stock, the less important the decreasing tack sequence becomes.

REMEDY: Reduce the tack of the ink that fails to trap properly. Secure inks for multicolor presswork with successively decreasing tacks.

Cause B: Inks improperly balanced as to color strength. This can result in having to run one color full and the following color spare, in which case the color run spare may not trap.

REMEDY: Any set of multicolor wet process inks should be balanced as to strength so that approximately equal amounts can be run. Use caution in running inks from different sets together.

14. Slur in Halftones and at the Back Edge of Solids

Slurring of halftones can be caused by too much back-cylinder pressure in printing coated stocks, by too much plate-to-blanket pressure in printing from smooth, ungrained plates, and by the rippling of unflat sheets as they enter the impression nip. It can also be caused by running too much ink on coated papers.

Slurring troubles are discussed in Section 2, page 28.

15. Prints are Mottled

The causes of mottling are not too well understood. The most likely causes are:

Cause A: Ink not properly adjusted to the stock.

REMEDIES: Increase the tack and length of the ink by adding body gum or water-resistant varnish. If this does not help, try a little grease or wax compound, or cornstarch.

Cause B: Non-ink-receptive stock.

REMEDY: Use an ink with maximum color strength and tack, and run it spare. Sometimes a little reducing compound helps.

Cause C: Uncoated stock with wild formation.

REMEDY: Use an ink with maximum color strength and minimum penetration.

Cause D: Coatings with non-uniform ink absorbency. This can be shown by the K & N Ink Absorbency Test (LTF Publication No. 308, page 138).

REMEDY: Add a little body gum or gloss varnish to make the ink less penetrating so it can dry with a uniform finish.

Figure 66. Mottled Solid on Paper with a "Wild" Formation and Uneven Absorbency

Cause E: Running too much ink on hard, non-ink-receptive papers.

REMEDY: Use an ink with greater color strength and run less of it.

Cause F: Excessive back-cylinder pressure.

REMEDY: Reduce the pressure. Stiffening the ink may help.

Cause G: Too much dampening water. Moisture reduces the ink's tack so that it squashes more easily. It also causes minute white spots in solids (snowflakiness).

REMEDY: Keep the dampening water to a minimum.

16. Color Fades or Burns Out During Drying

This trouble usually occurs in printing large solids or solid tints.

Cause: Not enough oxygen for complete drying. Once drying starts, the ink vehicle is so hungry that, when the available oxygen is used up, it will take the oxygen from certain pigments with the result that their color is bleached or burned out. Heat generated during drying accelerates this reaction.

REMEDY 1: When printing large solids, check with the ink maker. If the colors are susceptible to burning out, wind the printed sheets two or three times during the first four hours after printing.

REMEDY 2: Use inks that do not burn out.

17. Ghost Images Appear in Solids

Cause: A narrow solid ahead of or behind a wider solid is robbing the form roller of the ink needed to print full strength color in a corresponding area of the wider solid. Lateral distribution does not provide the extra ink in narrow sections needed to prevent ghosting.

REMEDY 1: Whenever possible, make layouts with solids well distributed.

REMEDY 2: Run a minimum of dampening water.

REMEDY 3: Avoid running colors spare to produce tints. Make the color weaker and run more of it.

REMEDY 4: If possible, use opaque inks for solid tints rather than transparent inks.

Figure 67.   Ghosting in a Solid Area Due to Ink Starvation in a Narrow
Band

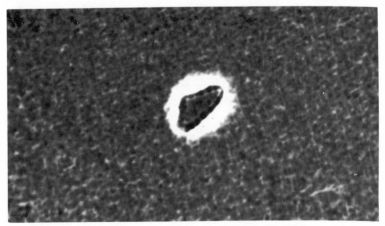

Figure 68.   Blow-up of a Typical Ink-skin Hicky

18. Ink-Skin Hickies

Cause: Particles of dried ink or drier mixed into the ink. They are the result of carelessness in ink making or in handling ink in the pressroom. They cannot be dispersed by grinding or removed from ink once they are mixed into it. The only remedy for hicky trouble is prevention.

Precautions to avoid hickies:
1. Care in removing ink from the can or kit.
2. Care of the ink remaining in the can or kit to avoid air pockets and bubbles.
3. Careful cleaning of the press before inking up to be sure there is no dried ink in the fountain or on the rollers.
4. Care in manipulating ink in the press fountain to avoid mixing into it any skin that may have formed around the edges of the ink mass.

19. Ink Flies or Mists

When ink flies, it forms fine droplets or filaments that pervade the atmosphere of the pressroom. Ink flying can be either an ink or a press problem.

Cause A: Too much ink. The thicker the ink film on the press rollers, the longer the filaments formed when it is split between rollers.

REMEDY: Substitute a more strongly colored ink and run less of it.

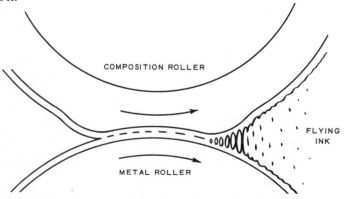

Figure 69.   Diagram Showing how an Ink Film can Split as it Emerges from the Roller Nip and Form Flying Particles

Cause B: The fountain is feeding too thick a film of ink to the fountain roller.

REMEDY: Tighten the fountain blade and adjust the ratchet to give the roller more movement.

Cause C: The ink is too long and too tacky.

REMEDY: Add a shortening material such as a wax compound. Consult the ink maker.

Cause D: Not enough lateral distribution. Too little sidewise motion of the vibrating drums allows the ink to form ridges on the rollers and increases its tendency to fly.

REMEDY: Increase the vibration until the ridging disappears.

INDEX

105

GATF Textbooks

The Lithographers Manual, Revised, Single Volume, 1966

308 What the Lithographer Should Know About Paper

310 What the Lithographer Should Know About Ink

319 Pick Tester

320 LTF Color Chart Book

321 Instruments for Quality Control

401 Chemistry of Lithography

402 Physics for Lithographers

501 Offset Press Troubles (Sheetfed Presses)

502/4 Offset Platemaking

503 Offset Photography (Line)

505/6 Offset Press Operating

507 Offset Stripping (Black and White)

508 Offset Photography (Halftone)

509 Offset Photography (Color Separation)

510/11 Tone and Color Correcting

512 Color Stripping

513 Advanced Pressmanship (Sheetfed Presses)

515 Photo-Composing

517 Web Offset Press Troubles

518 Contact Printing